Embedded Linux Development with Yocto Project

Develop fascinating Linux-based projects using the groundbreaking Yocto Project tools

Otavio Salvador

Daiane Angolini

BIRMINGHAM - MUMBAI

Embedded Linux Development with Yocto Project

First published: July 2014

Production reference: 1020714

Published by Packt Publishing Ltd.
Livery Place
35 Livery Street
Birmingham B3 2PB, UK.

ISBN 978-1-78328-233-3

www.packtpub.com

Cover image by Jarek Blaminsky (milak6@wp.pl)

Credits

Authors
Otavio Salvador
Daiane Angolini

Reviewers
Radek Dostál
Alex González
Rogerio Nunes
Jeffrey Osier-Mixon
Alexandru Vaduva

Commissioning Editor
Aarthi Kumaraswamy

Acquisition Editor
Harsha Bharwani

Content Development Editor
Sankalp Pawar

Technical Editor
Manan Badani

Copy Editor
Sayanee Mukherjee

Project Coordinators
Harshal Ved
Sageer Parkar

Proofreaders
Simran Bhogal
Stephen Copestake
Amy Guest

Indexers
Hemangini Bari
Mariammal Chettiyar
Tejal Soni

Graphics
Sheetal Aute
Valentina Dsilva
Abhinash Sahu

Production Coordinator
Alwin Roy

Cover Work
Alwin Roy

About the Authors

Otavio Salvador loves to play video games and started his free software activities in 1999. In 2002, he founded O.S. Systems, a company focused on embedded system development services and consultancy worldwide, creating and maintaining customized BSPs and helping companies with their release management challenges. This resulted in him joining the OpenEmbedded community in 2008, when he became an active contributor to the OpenEmbedded project, culminating in his attribution as the maintainer of the Freescale ARM BSP layer in the Yocto Project in 2011.

Daiane Angolini has been focusing on embedded technologies for the past 8 years. Since 2008, she has been working on Freescale Semiconductors as an application engineer, on internal development and porting custom applications from Android to Freescale architectures, and on customer support for ARM processors of the i.MX family, while also participating in Freescale forums. She has been working with the Yocto Project tools through meta-fsl-arm, the BSP meta layer that provides board support for Freescale ARM machines, since 2012. The desire to become an expert in ice cream making has been keeping her busy in her spare time for the past year.

We initially want to thank our families. They provided lovely support and helped us to get on track for this project.

This project has only been possible because we had support from many people who provided insights, reviews, material, and guidance during the full period of conception and production of this book. We'd like to give special thanks to (in alphabetic order): Alex González, Alexandru Vaduva, Harsha Bharwani, Jeffrey Osier-Mixon, John Weber, Manan Badani, Paul Eggleton, Rogerio Nunes, Radek Dostál, Sageer Parkar, and Sankalp Pawar

- Otavio Salvador and Daiane Angolini

About the Reviewers

Radek Dostál is a fan of Linux and has been using it for the last 15 years. During his exchange studies in the US, he acquired a passion for embedded systems, and combining Linux with embedded systems has been his bread and butter ever since. The Yocto Project has had a great impact on Radek's work; he managed to persuade his team and managers to switch to Yocto Project for an important project, thus building a solid foundation for several successful follow-up projects. Radek likes to contribute to open source projects as part of his work as well as during his free time. However, if the weather is good during the weekend, you are most likely to find him in the mountains.

Alex González is Principal Software Engineer at Digi International and one of the maintainers of Digi Embedded Yocto distribution.

He started working professionally with embedded systems in 1999 and the Linux kernel in 2004, designing products for next-generation IP networks in the UK start-up scene, and he followed his interests into M2M and the Internet of Things.

Born and raised in Spain, he has his second home in the UK, where he lived for over 10 years and received his MSc degree in Communication Systems from the University of Portsmouth. Alex currently lives in La Rioja, Spain, where he is known to enjoy photography and a good Riojan wine.

Rogerio Nunes has over 11 years of experience in embedded systems. He received his MS (2009) and BS (2004) in Electrical Engineering from the University of São Paulo in Brazil, where he also worked for 8 years in research and development. In 2011, Rogerio started his career at Freescale in São Paulo as a Field Applications Engineer (FAE), supporting high-end multimedia SoCs. Later in 2012, Rogerio moved to Boston in the same role as FAE for the same company. Rogerio's fields of expertise include digital TV, multimedia, video coding, and software development. In these areas, Rogerio has developed systems with different technologies (from VHDL to high-level software), and he has also led development teams.

Jeffrey Osier-Mixon is a Yocto Project community manager. He has been working directly with Linux since the late 1990s and with embedded systems and open source software for over 20 years, most often as a technical writer and editor, freelance writer and journalist, and community manager. He has been a regular speaker at open source conferences worldwide since 2008. He is employed by Intel Corporation to help the Yocto Project succeed.

> I would like to thank Otavio and Daiane for writing this book and giving me the opportunity to review it. I am sure it will be a valuable asset to the Yocto Project community.

Alexandru Vaduva is an embedded Linux software engineer, focused on open source and free software. He has an inquisitive mind and also believes that actions can speak more about someone than their own words. He is a strong supporter of the idea that there is no need to reinvent the wheel, but there is always room for improvement.

His knowledge background includes C, Yocto, Linux, Bash, and Python, but he is also open to trying new things and testing new technologies.

> Big thanks to all the people who believed in me, and the open source communities that helped me evolve and kept me motivated.

www.PacktPub.com

Support files, eBooks, discount offers, and more

You might want to visit www.PacktPub.com for support files and downloads related to your book.

Did you know that Packt offers eBook versions of every book published, with PDF and ePub files available? You can upgrade to the eBook version at www.PacktPub.com and as a print book customer, you are entitled to a discount on the eBook copy. Get in touch with us at service@packtpub.com for more details.

At www.PacktPub.com, you can also read a collection of free technical articles, sign up for a range of free newsletters and receive exclusive discounts and offers on Packt books and eBooks.

http://PacktLib.PacktPub.com

Do you need instant solutions to your IT questions? PacktLib is Packt's online digital book library. Here, you can access, read and search across Packt's entire library of books.

Why subscribe?

- Fully searchable across every book published by Packt
- Copy and paste, print and bookmark content
- On demand and accessible via web browser

Free access for Packt account holders

If you have an account with Packt at www.PacktPub.com, you can use this to access PacktLib today and view nine entirely free books. Simply use your login credentials for immediate access.

Table of Contents

Preface

Considering the current technology trend, Linux is the next big thing. Linux has consistently released cutting-edge open source products, and embedded systems have been added to the technological portfolio of mankind.

The Yocto Project is in an optimal position to be the choice for your projects; it provides a rich set of tools to help you to use most of your energy and resources in your product development, instead of reinventing the wheel.

The usual tasks and requirements for embedded Linux-based products and development teams were the guidelines for this book's conception. Written by active community members with a practical and straightforward approach, it is a stepping stone for both your learning curve and your product's project.

What this book covers

Chapter 1, Meeting the Yocto Project, presents the history of the Yocto Project, showing the parts that compose it.

Chapter 2, Baking Our Poky-based System, introduces the environment needed for the first build.

Chapter 3, Using Hob to Bake an Image, shows the user-friendly graphical interface that can be used as a wrapper for configuration and as a build tool.

Chapter 4, Grasping the BitBake Tool, presents the first concepts and premises of the tool used to control all other pieces of the Yocto Project.

Chapter 5, Detailing the Temporary Build Directory, details the output directory tree of a build with focus on the tmp directory.

Chapter 6, Assimilating Packaging Support, introduces the package concepts and details the packaging support used by the Yocto Project.

Chapter 7, Diving into BitBake Metadata, details the concepts and syntaxes used by the Yocto Project metadata, both in recipes and configuration files.

Chapter 8, Developing with the Yocto Project, details how to use the Yocto Project to generate a custom development environment.

Chapter 9, Debugging with the Yocto Project, details which debug tools the Yocto Project provides and how to use them.

Chapter 10, Exploring External Layers, explores one of the most important concepts of the Yocto Project, which is the flexibility of using external layers.

Chapter 11, Creating Custom Layers, practices the steps of creation of layers.

Chapter 12, Customizing Existing Recipes, lists the common use cases of recipe customization and how to achieve them properly.

Chapter 13, Achieving GPL Compliance, summarizes the tasks and concepts involved in a copyleft compliance product.

Chapter 14, Booting Our Custom Embedded Linux, uses a real hardware machine together with the Yocto Project's tools.

Appendix, References, lists the references used in the book.

What you need for this book

To better understand this book, it is important that you have some previous background in some topics that are not covered or are just briefly mentioned along the text.

A basic understanding of the GNU/Linux environment usage and embedded Linux is important along with general concepts used in development as compilation, debugging, deployment, and installation. Some experience with Shell Script and Python is a bonus because these programming languages are core technologies used extensively by the Yocto Project's tools.

However, the concepts enumerated should not discourage you from reading this book as they can be learned concurrently.

Who this book is for

This book is intended to be read by engineers and enthusiasts with embedded Linux experience willing to learn the Yocto Project's tools for evaluation, comparison, or use in a project. This book is aimed to get you up to speed quickly and to prevent you from getting trapped by the usual learning curve pitfalls.

Conventions

In this book, you will find a number of styles of text that distinguish between different kinds of information. Here are some examples of these styles, and an explanation of their meaning.

Code words in text, database table names, folder names, filenames, file extensions, pathnames, dummy URLs, user input, and Twitter handles are shown as follows: "Throughout the book, we will use build as the build directory."

A block of code is set as follows:

```
BB_NUMBER_THREADS ?= "${@oe.utils.cpu_count()}"
PARALLEL_MAKE ?= "-j ${@oe.utils.cpu_count()}"
MACHINE ??= "qemux86"
```

Any command-line input or output is written as follows:

```
$: sudo apt-get install gawk wget git-core diffstat unzip texinfo
build-essential chrpath
```

New terms and **important words** are shown in bold. Words that you see on the screen, in menus or dialog boxes for example, appear in the text like this: "If we plan to build a standard image, we can click on **Build Image** and wait for BitBake to run the required tasks to build it."

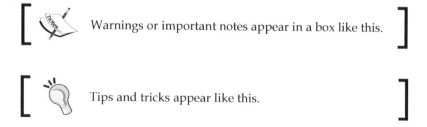

Warnings or important notes appear in a box like this.

Tips and tricks appear like this.

Reader feedback

Feedback from our readers is always welcome. Let us know what you think about this book—what you liked or may have disliked. Reader feedback is important for us to develop titles that you really get the most out of.

To send us general feedback, simply send an e-mail to feedback@packtpub.com, and mention the book title via the subject of your message.

If there is a topic that you have expertise in and you are interested in either writing or contributing to a book, see our author guide on www.packtpub.com/authors.

Customer support

Now that you are the proud owner of a Packt book, we have a number of things to help you to get the most from your purchase.

Downloading the color images of the book

We also provide you a PDF file that has color images of the screenshots/diagrams used in this book. The color images will help you better understand the changes in the output. You can download this file from: https://www.packtpub.com/sites/default/files/downloads/2333OS_ColoredImages.pdf

Errata

Although we have taken every care to ensure the accuracy of our content, mistakes do happen. If you find a mistake in one of our books—maybe a mistake in the text or the code—we would be grateful if you would report this to us. By doing so, you can save other readers from frustration and help us improve subsequent versions of this book. If you find any errata, please report them by visiting http://www.packtpub.com/submit-errata, selecting your book, clicking on the **errata submission form** link, and entering the details of your errata. Once your errata are verified, your submission will be accepted and the errata will be uploaded on our website, or added to any list of existing errata, under the Errata section of that title. Any existing errata can be viewed by selecting your title from http://www.packtpub.com/support.

Piracy

Piracy of copyright material on the Internet is an ongoing problem across all media. At Packt, we take the protection of our copyright and licenses very seriously. If you come across any illegal copies of our works, in any form, on the Internet, please provide us with the location address or website name immediately so that we can pursue a remedy.

Please contact us at copyright@packtpub.com with a link to the suspected pirated material.

We appreciate your help in protecting our authors, and our ability to bring you valuable content.

Questions

You can contact us at questions@packtpub.com if you are having a problem with any aspect of the book, and we will do our best to address it.

Meeting the Yocto Project

1

In this chapter, we will be introduced to the **Yocto Project**. The main concepts of the project, which are constantly used throughout the book, are discussed here. We will discuss the Yocto Project history, OpenEmbedded, Poky, BitBake, and Metadata in brief, so fasten your seat belt and welcome aboard!

What is the Yocto Project?

The Yocto Project is a Linux Foundation workgroup defined as:

> "*The Yocto Project provides open source, high-quality infrastructure and tools to help developers create their own custom Linux distributions for any hardware architecture, across multiple market segments. The Yocto Project is intended to provide a helpful starting point for developers.*"

The Yocto Project is an open source collaboration project that provides templates, tools, and methods to help us create custom Linux-based systems for embedded products regardless of the hardware architecture. Being managed by a Linux Foundation fellow, the project remains independent of its member organizations that participate in various ways and provide resources to the project.

It was founded in 2010 as a collaboration of many hardware manufacturers, open source operating systems, vendors, and electronics companies in an effort to reduce their work duplication, providing resources and information catering to both new and experienced users.

Among these resources is OpenEmbedded-Core, the core system component, provided by the OpenEmbedded project.

The Yocto Project is, therefore, a community open source project that aggregates several companies, communities, projects, and tools, gathering people with the same purpose to build a Linux-based embedded product; all these components are in the same boat, being driven by its community needs to work together.

Delineating the Yocto Project

To ease our understanding of the duties and outcomes provided by the Yocto Project, we can use the analogy of a computing machine. The input is a set of data that describes what we want, that is, our specification. As an output, we have the desired Linux-based embedded product.

If the output is a product running a Linux-based operating system, the result generated is the pieces that compose the operating system, such as the Linux kernel, bootloader, and the root filesystem (`rootfs`) bundle, which are properly organized.

To produce the resultant `rootfs` bundle and other deliverables, the Yocto Project's tools are present in all intermediary steps. The reuse of previously built utilities and other software components are maximized while building other applications, libraries, and any other software components in the right order and with the desired configuration, including the fetching of the required source code from their respective repositories such as The Linux Kernel Archives (`www.kernel.org`), GitHub, and `www.SourceForge.net`.

Preparing its own build environment, utilities, and toolchain, the amount of host software dependency is reduced, but a more important implication is that the determinism is considerably increased. The utilities, versions, and configuration options are the same, minimizing the number of host utilities to rely on.

We can list some projects, such as Poky, BitBake, and OpenEmbedded-Core, under the Yocto Project umbrella, all of them being complimentary and playing specific roles in the system. We will understand exactly how they work together in this chapter and throughout the book.

Understanding Poky

Poky is the Yocto Project reference system and is composed of a collection of tools and metadata. It is platform-independent and performs cross-compiling, using the **BitBake** tool, OpenEmbedded Core, and a default set of metadata, as shown in the following figure. It provides the mechanism to build and combine thousands of distributed open source projects to form a fully customizable, complete, and coherent Linux software stack.

Poky's main objective is to provide all the features an embedded developer needs.

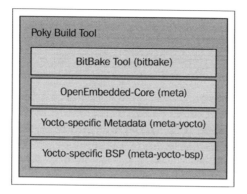

Using BitBake

BitBake is a task scheduler that parses Python and Shell Script mixed code. The code parsed generates and runs tasks, which are basically a set of steps ordered according to the code's dependencies.

It evaluates all available configuration files and recipe data (known as **metadata**), managing dynamic variable expansion, dependencies, and code generation. It keeps track of all tasks being processed in order to ensure completion, maximizing the use of processing resources to reduce build time and being predictable. The development of BitBake is centralized in the `bitbake-devel@lists.openembedded.org` mailing list, and its code can be found in the `bitbake` subdirectory of Poky.

OpenEmbedded-Core

The **OpenEmbedded-Core** metadata collection provides the engine of the Poky build tool. It is designed to provide the core features and needs to be as clean as possible. It provides support for five different processor architectures (**ARM, x86, x86-64, PowerPC, MIPS** and **MIPS64**), supporting only QEMU-emulated machines.

The development is centralized in the `openembedded-core@lists.openembedded.org` mailing list, and houses its metadata inside the `meta` subdirectory of Poky.

Metadata

The metadata, which is composed of a mix of Python and Shell Script text files, provides a tremendously flexible system. Poky uses this to extend OpenEmbedded-Core and includes two different layers, which are another metadata subset shown as follows:

- `meta-yocto`: This layer provides the default and supported distributions, visual branding, and metadata tracking information (maintainers, upstream status, and so on)
- `meta-yocto-bsp`: This layer, on top of it, provides the hardware reference boards support for use in Poky

Chapter 7, Diving into BitBake Metadata, explores the metadata in more detail and serves as a reference when we write our own recipes.

The alliance of OpenEmbedded Project and Yocto Project

The **OpenEmbedded** project was created around January 2003 when some core developers from the **OpenZaurus** project started to work with the new build system. The OpenEmbedded build system has been, since its beginning, a tasks scheduler inspired and based on the **Gentoo Portage** package system named BitBake. The project has grown its software collection, and a number of supported machines at a fast pace.

As consequence of uncoordinated development, it is difficult to use OpenEmbedded in products that demand a more stable and polished code base, which is why Poky was born. Poky started as a subset of OpenEmbedded and had a more polished and stable code base across a limited set of architectures. This reduced size allowed Poky to start to develop highlighting technologies, such as IDE plugins and QEMU integration, which are still being used today.

Around November 2010, the Yocto Project was announced by the Linux Foundation to continue this work under a Linux Foundation-sponsored project. The Yocto Project and OpenEmbedded Project consolidated their efforts on a core build system called OpenEmbedded-Core, using the best of both Poky and OpenEmbedded, emphasizing an increased use of additional components, metadata, and subsets.

Summary

This first chapter provided an overview on how the OpenEmbedded Project is related to the Yocto Project, the components which form Poky, and how it was created. In the next chapter, we will be introduced to the Poky workflow with steps to download, configure, and prepare the Poky build environment, and how to have the very first image built and running using QEMU.

2
Baking Our Poky-based System

In this chapter, we will understand the basic concepts involved in the Poky workflow. Let's get our hands dirty with steps to download and configure, prepare the Poky build environment, and bake something usable. The steps covered here are commonly used for testing and development. They give us the whole experience of using Poky and a taste of its capabilities.

Configuring a host system

The process needed to set up our host system depends on the distribution we run on it. Poky has a set of supported Linux distributions, and if we are new to embedded Linux development, it is advisable to use one of the supported Linux distributions to avoid wasting time debugging build issues related to the host system support. Currently, the supported distributions are the following:

- Ubuntu 12.04 (LTS)
- Ubuntu 13.10
- Ubuntu 14.04 (LTS)
- Fedora release 19 (Schrödinger's Cat)
- Fedora release 20 (Heisenbug)
- CentOS release 6.4
- CentOS release 6.5
- Debian GNU/Linux 7.x (Wheezy)
- openSUSE 12.2

- openSUSE 12.3
- openSUSE 13.1

If our preferred distribution is not in the preceding list, it doesn't mean it is not possible to use Poky on it. However, it is unknown whether it will work, and we may get unexpected results.

The packages that need to be installed into the host system vary from one distribution to another. Throughout this book, you find instructions for **Debian** and **Fedora**, our preferred distributions. You can find the instructions for all supported distributions in the *Yocto Project Reference Manual*.

Installing Poky on Debian

To install the needed packages for a headless host system, run the following command:

```
$: sudo apt-get install gawk wget git-core diffstat unzip texinfo
build-essential chrpath
```

If our host system has graphics support, run the following command:

```
$: sudo apt-get install libsdl1.2-dev xterm
```

The preceding commands are also compatible with the Ubuntu distributions.

Installing Poky on Fedora

To install the needed packages for a headless host system, run the following command:

```
$: sudo yum install gawk make wget tar bzip2 gzip python unzip perl
patch diffutils diffstat git cpp gcc gcc-c++ eglibc-devel texinfo
chrpath ccache
```

If our host system has graphics support, run the following command:

```
$: sudo yum install SDL-devel xterm
```

Downloading the Poky source code

After we install the needed packages into our development host system, we need to get the Poky source code that can be downloaded with Git, using the following command:

```
$: git clone git://git.yoctoproject.org/poky --branch daisy
```

Learn more about Git at `http://git-scm.com`.

After the download process is complete, we should have the following contents inside the `poky` directory:

```
●  ─  □   Content of Poky directory after download
$: ls -l
total 68
drwxr-xr-x  6 user user  4096 Mai 12 11:06 bitbake
drwxr-xr-x 12 user user  4096 Mai 12 11:06 documentation
-rw-r--r--  1 user user   515 Mai 12 11:06 LICENSE
drwxr-xr-x 21 user user  4096 Mai 12 11:06 meta
drwxr-xr-x  5 user user  4096 Mai 12 11:06 meta-selftest
drwxr-xr-x  7 user user  4096 Mai 12 11:06 meta-skeleton
drwxr-xr-x  5 user user  4096 Mai 12 11:06 meta-yocto
drwxr-xr-x  7 user user  4096 Mai 12 11:06 meta-yocto-bsp
-rwxrwxr-x  1 user user  2000 Mai 12 11:06 oe-init-build-env
-rwxr-xr-x  1 user user  2449 Mai 12 11:06 oe-init-build-env-memres
-rw-r--r--  1 user user  2046 Mai 12 11:06 README
-rw-rw-r--  1 user user 18500 Mai 12 11:06 README.hardware
drwxr-xr-x  9 user user  4096 Mai 12 11:06 scripts
$:
```

 The examples and code presented in this and the next chapters use the Yocto Project Version 1.6 and Poky Version 11.0. The code name is Daisy, as reference.

Preparing the build environment

Inside the `poky` directory, there is a script named `oe-init-build-env`, which should be used to set up the build environment. The script must be run as shown:

```
$: source poky/oe-init-build-env [build-directory]
```

Here, `build-directory` is an optional parameter for the name of the directory where the environment is set; in case it is not given, it defaults to `build`. The `build-directory` is the place where we perform the builds.

It is very convenient to use different build directories. We can work on distinct projects in parallel or different experimental setups without affecting our other builds.

Throughout the book, we will use `build` as the build directory. When we need to point to a file inside the build directory, we will adopt the same convention, for example, `build/conf/local.conf`.

Knowing the local.conf file

When we initialize a build environment, it creates a file called `build/conf/local.conf`, which is a powerful tool that can configure almost every aspect of the build process. We can set the machine we are building for, choose the toolchain host architecture to be used for a custom cross-toolchain, optimize options for maximum build time reduction, and so on. The comments inside the `build/conf/local.conf` file are a very good documentation and reference of possible variables, and their defaults. The minimal set of variables we probably want to change from the default is the following:

```
BB_NUMBER_THREADS ?= "${@oe.utils.cpu_count()}"
PARALLEL_MAKE ?= "-j ${@oe.utils.cpu_count()}"
MACHINE ??= "qemux86"
```

 `BB_NUMBER_THREADS` and `PARALLEL_MAKE` should be set to twice the host processor's number of cores.

The `MACHINE` variable is where we determine the target machine we wish to build for. At the time of writing this book, Poky supports the following machines in its reference **Board Support Package (BSP)**:

- `beaglebone`: This is BeagleBone
- `genericx86`: This is a generic support for 32-bit x86-based machines
- `genericx86-64`: This is a generic support for 64-bit x86-based machines
- `mpc8315e-rdb`: This is a freescale MPC8315 PowerPC reference platform
- `edgerouter`: This is Edgerouter Lite

The machines are made available by a layer called `meta-yocto-bsp`. Besides these machines, OpenEmbedded-Core also provides support for the following:

- `qemuarm`: This is the QEMU ARM emulation
- `qemumips`: This is the QEMU MIPS emulation
- `qemumips64`: This is the QEMU MIPS64 emulation
- `qemuppc`: This is the QEMU PowerPC emulation

- `qemux86-64`: This is the QEMU x86-64 emulation

- `qemux86`: This is the QEMU x86 emulation

Other machines are supported through extra BSP layers and these are available from a number of vendors. The process of using an extra BSP layer is shown in *Chapter 10, Exploring External Layers*.

> The `local.conf` file is a very convenient way to override several default configurations over all the Yocto Project's tools. Essentially, we can change or set any variable, for example, add additional packages to an image file.
>
> Though it is convenient, it should be considered as a temporary change as the `build/conf/local.conf` file is not usually tracked by any source code management system.

Building a target image

Poky provides several predesigned image recipes that we can use to build our own binary image. We can check the list of available images running the following command from the `poky` directory:

```
$: ls meta*/recipes*/images/*.bb
```

All the recipes provide images which are, in essence, a set of unpacked and configured packages, generating a filesystem that we can use on an actual hardware.

Next, we can see a short description of available images, as follows:

- `build-appliance-image`: This is a virtual machine image which can be run by either VMware Player or VMware Workstation that allows to run builds.

- `core-image-full-cmdline`: This is a console-only image with full support for the target device hardware.

- `core-image-minimal`: This is a small image allowing a device to boot, and it is very useful for kernel and boot loader tests and development.

- `core-image-minimal-dev`: This image includes all contents of the `core-image-minimal` image and adds headers and libraries that we can use in a host development environment.

- `core-image-minimal-initramfs`: This `core-image-minimal` image is used for minimal RAM-based initial root filesystem (`initramfs`) and as a part of the kernel.

- `core-image-minimal-mtdutils`: This is a `core-image-minimal` image that has support for the MTD utilities for use with flash devices.

- `core-image-full-cmdline`: This is a console-only image with more full-featured Linux system functionalities installed.

- `core-image-lsb`: This is an image that conforms to the **Linux Standard Base (LSB)** specification.

- `core-image-lsb-dev`: This is a `core-image-lsb` image that is suitable for development work using the host, since it includes headers and libraries that we can use in a host development environment.

- `core-image-lsb-sdk`: This is a `core-image-lsb` image that includes a complete standalone SDK. This image is suitable for development using the target.

- `core-image-clutter`: This is an image with clutter support that enables development of rich and animated graphical user interfaces.

- `core-image-directfb`: This is an image that uses DirectFB instead of X11.

- `core-image-weston`: This is an image that provides the Wayland protocol libraries and the reference Weston compositor.

- `core-image-x11`: This is a very basic X11 image with a terminal.

- `qt4e-demo-image`: This is an image that launches into the Qt Demo application for the embedded (not based on X11) version of Qt.

- `core-image-rt`: This is a `core-image-minimal` image plus a real-time test suite and tool appropriate for real-time use.

- `core-image-rt-sdk`: This is a `core-image-rt` image that includes a complete standalone SDK and is suitable for development using the target.

- `core-image-sato`: This is an image with Sato support and a mobile environment for mobile devices that use X11; it provides applications such as a terminal, editor, file manager, media player, and so forth.

- `core-image-sato-dev`: This is a `core-image-sato` image that includes libraries needed to build applications on the device itself, testing and profiling tools and debugging symbols.

- `core-image-sato-sdk`: This is a `core-image-sato` image that includes a complete standalone SDK and is suitable for development using the target.

- `core-image-multilib-example`: This is an example image that includes a lib32 version of Bash, otherwise it is a standard Sato image.

The up-to-date image list can be seen in the *Yocto Project Reference Manual*.

The process of building an image for a target is very simple. We must run the following command:

```
$: bitbake <recipe name>
```

For example, to build `core-image-full-cmdline`, run the following command:

```
$: bitbake core-image-full-cmdline
```

 We will use `MACHINE = "qemuarm"` in the following examples. It should be set in `build/conf/local.conf` accordingly.

Running images in QEMU

As many projects have a small portion that is hardware dependent, the hardware emulation comes to speed up the development process by enabling sample to run without involving an actual hardware.

Quick EMUlator (QEMU) is a free and open source software package that performs hardware virtualization. The QEMU-based machines allow test and development without real hardware. Currently, the ARM, MIPS, MIPS64, PowerPC, and x86 and x86-64 emulations are supported.

The `runqemu` script enables and makes the use of QEMU with the OpenEmbedded-Core supported machines easier. The way to run the script is as follows:

```
$: runqemu <machine> <zimage> <filesystems>
```

Here, `<machine>` is the machine/architecture to be used as `qemuarm`, `qemumips`, `qemuppc`, `qemux86`, or `qemux86-64`. Also, `<zimage>` is the path to a kernel (for example, `zimage-qemuarm.bin`). Finally, `<filesystem>` is the path to an `ext3` image (for example, `filesystem-qemuarm.ext3`) or an NFS directory.

So, for example, in case we run `runqemu qemuarm core-image-full-cmdline`, we can see something as shown in the following screenshot:

```
⊗ – □   QEMU - Press Ctrl-Alt to exit mouse grab
Freeing unused kernel memory: 332K (c0827000 - c087a000)
INIT: version 2.88 booting
Starting udev
Starting Bootlog daemon: bootlogd.
Populating dev cache
net.ipv4.conf.default.rp_filter = 1
net.ipv4.conf.all.rp_filter = 1
Starting atd: OK
INIT: Entering runlevel: 5
Configuring network interfaces... done.
Starting system message bus: dbus.
Starting OpenBSD Secure Shell server: sshd
  generating ssh RSA key...
  generating ssh ECDSA key...
  generating ssh DSA key...
  generating ssh ED25519 key...
done.
Starting rpcbind daemon...done.
creating NFS state directory: done
starting statd: done
starting 8 nfsd kernel threads: done
starting mountd: done
Starting system log daemon...0
Starting kernel log daemon...0
Starting Lighttpd Web Server: lighttpd.
Starting crond: OK
Stopping Bootlog daemon:
Poky (Yocto Project Reference Distro) 1.6 qemuarm /dev/tty1

qemuarm login: _
```

We can log in with the root account using an empty password. The system behaves as a regular system even being used inside the QEMU. The process to deploy an image in a real hardware varies depending on the type of storage used, bootloader, and so on. However, the process to generate the image is the same. We explore how to build and run an image in the Wandboard machine in *Chapter 14, Booting Our Custom Embedded Linux*.

Summary

In this chapter, we learned the steps needed to set up Poky and get our first image built. We ran that image using `runqemu`, which gave us a good overview of the available capabilities.

In the next chapter, we will be introduced to **Hob**, which provides a human friendly interface for BitBake, and we will use it to build an image and customize it further.

Using Hob to Bake an Image

3

Hob is a human friendly interface for BitBake. It helps us customize images and have them the way we want. It also enables us to run the image on QEMU after *bitbaking* it. It is just like a bakery display; we can pick what we want and use it right away.

Building an image using Hob

Our first step is to set up our build environment, as follows:

```
$: source poky/oe-init-build-env [build-directory]
```

We can choose an old build directory or create a new one.

Now, Hob is ready for use. To start it, we should run the following:

```
$: hob
```

At startup, Hob performs some parsing tasks, reading the local configuration and available metadata layers. After a short time, Hob proposes a list of available machines. We can select, for example, `qemuarm`.

Once the dependency tree is built, select the desired image, for example, `core-image-full-cmdline`.

The following screenshot shows the MACHINE variable content and the image to be built in the Hob interface:

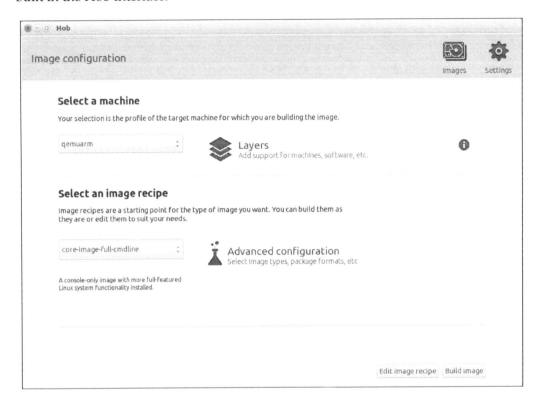

With the target MACHINE and image selected, the next step is to choose some advanced configuration, such as image types (for example, cpio.gz, ext2.bz2, ext3.gz, jffs2, ubifs, and vmdk) or package formats (rpm, deb, IPK, or TAR). We can also exclude all packages under the **GPLv3** licensing, as shown in *Chapter 13, Achieving GPL Compliance*.

From the upper-right hand corner of the window, we can access the two areas **Images** and **Settings**. **Images** offers access to the built images (from the past), and **Settings** performs changes to MACHINE, parallelization, distribution, shared folders, and BBLAYERS. Hob modifies the build/conf directory contents inside our build directory. We can use Hob on our already configured build folder, and all configurations are reflected on Hob. It may be very useful when working on a team.

If we are working to configure the shared environment for a team, we need to pay attention to the variables DL_DIR and SSTATE_DIR, which are detailed in *Chapter 4, Grasping the BitBake Tool*, and *Chapter 6, Assimilating Packaging Support*.

If we plan to build a standard image, we can click on **Build Image** and wait for BitBake to run the required tasks to build it. Otherwise, if we want to change the recipe set of an image, we can click on **Edit image recipe**.

Customizing an image with Hob

The following screenshot shows the list of included recipes in the Hob interface:

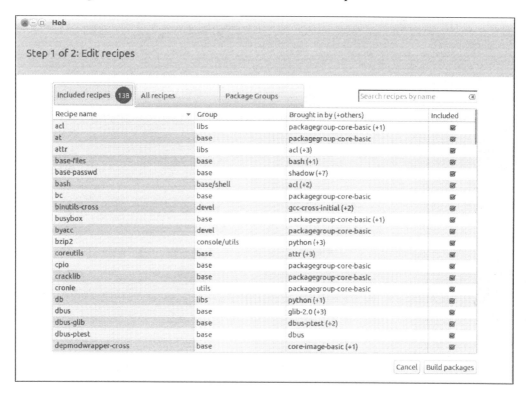

We can add or remove recipes (there is a search box in the upper-right hand corner) by selecting or deselecting them. If we click on the recipe name, we can see details such as its version and license.

From the tabs, we can see the number of selected packages, the list of available packages, and how the selected packages are grouped, as shown in the following screenshot:

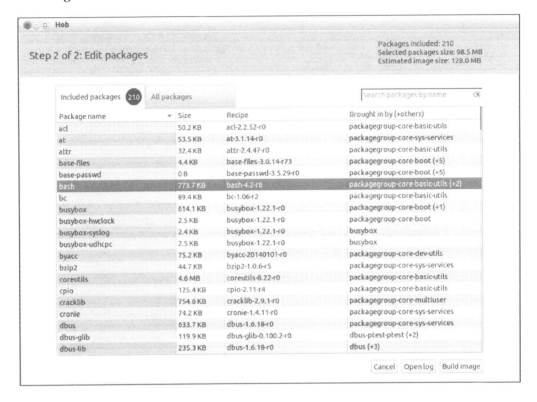

After clicking on **Build packages** and waiting for them to be built, we have a second chance to see the list of selected packages, to know the value of the **Estimated image size**, and to decide to remove some application in order to generate a smaller image. By clicking on the package name, the included files from this package are listed. If a package is highlighted, its log can be displayed by clicking on **Open log**.

BitBake resolves all dependencies from the selected packages, including any needed additional package.

We can wrap the image by clicking on **Build image** and waiting until our image is ready, as shown in the following screenshot:

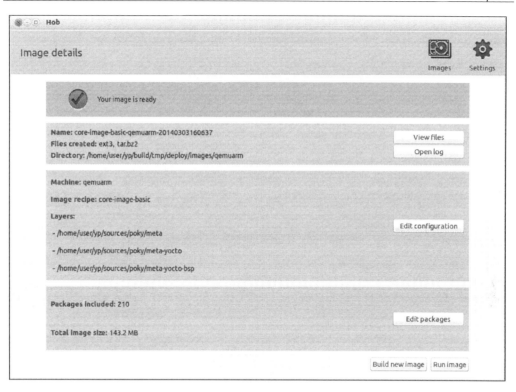

We can start over and change configurations, edit the selected packages, view logs, or list the files. Or, for images made for the QEMU-based machines, we can click on **Run image** and see our image being run inside the QEMU emulator, and the Yocto Project logo, as shown in the next screenshot:

Hob is a nice tool for image adjustments and addition of few packages on existing images. It is a great user-friendly interface for simple tasks and may be useful for teams to make temporary modifications in their images.

Hob is in the process of being replaced by a new tool called **Toaster**. At the time of writing this book, Toaster is under heavy development, and it is still feature incomplete. However, the next Yocto Project release will supersede Hob, according to the Toaster planned feature set. So, it is advised to research for Toaster in the Yocto Project documentation website for more updated information.

Summary

In this chapter, we learned about the different Hob functionalities and configurable variables. We learned how Hob can be used to easily make changes by teams and how it takes advantage of a user-friendly user interface for simple tasks.

In the next chapter, we will understand how BitBake does its magic. We will grasp the parsing, preferences and providers support, dependencies, task handling, and main task functions.

4
Grasping the BitBake Tool

We now start our journey to understand how the Yocto Project's engine works behind the scenes. In the preceding chapters, we were introduced to the usual Yocto Project workflow to create and emulate images.

In this chapter, we will understand the metadata concept and how recipes depend on each other, and are used by Poky. We will understand how BitBake downloads every needed source code package and how these packages are stored in the directory used to build. This chapter also lists the most common tasks used to generate packages, and determines how packages fit into generated images.

Understanding the BitBake tool

The BitBake task scheduler started as a fork from **Portage**, which is the package management system used in the **Gentoo** distribution. However, nowadays the two projects have diverged a lot due to the different usage focusses. The Yocto Project and the OpenEmbedded Project are the most known and intensive users of BitBake, which remains a separated and independent project with its own development cycle and mailing list (`bitbake-devel@lists.openembedded.org`).

As presented in *Chapter 1*, *Meeting the Yocto Project*, BitBake is a task scheduler that parses Python and the shell script mixed code. The code parsed generates and runs tasks that may have a complex dependency chain, which is scheduled to allow a parallel execution and maximize the use of computational resources. BitBake can be understood as a tool similar to **GNU Make** in some aspects.

In this chapter, we cover the main aspects of BitBake tool. However, for more in-depth details about the tool, please refer to the *BitBake User Manual*.

Exploring metadata

The metadata used by BitBake can be classified into three major areas:

- Configuration (the `.conf` files)
- Classes (the `.bbclass` files)
- Recipes (the `.bb` and `.bbappend` files)

The configuration files define the global content, which is used to provide information and configure how the recipes will work. One common example of the configuration file is the machine file that has a list of settings, which describes the board hardware.

The classes are used by the whole system and can be inherited by recipes, according to their needs or by default, as in this case with classes used to define the system behavior and provide the base methods. For example, `kernel.bbclass` helps the process of build, install, and package of the Linux kernel, independent of version and vendor.

 The recipes and classes are written in a mix of Python and shell scripting code.

The classes and recipes describe the tasks to be run and provide the needed information to allow BitBake to generate the needed task chain. The inheritance mechanism that permits a recipe to inherit one or more classes is useful to reduce code duplication, and eases the maintenance. A Linux kernel recipe example is `linux-yocto_3.14.bb`, which inherits a set of classes, including `kernel.bbclass`.

BitBake's most commonly used aspects across all types of metadata (`.conf`, `.bb`, and `.bbclass`) are shown in the following examples.

The metadata grammar and syntax are detailed in *Chapter 7, Diving into BitBake Metadata*.

Parsing metadata

As previously said, there are three metadata groups—configuration, class, and recipe.

The first parsed metadata in BitBake is configuration metadata, identified by the `.conf` file extension. This metadata is global, and therefore, affects all recipes and tasks which are executed.

BitBake first searches the current working directory for an optional `build/conf/bblayers.conf` configuration file, and it is expected to contain a `BBLAYERS` variable that is a space-delimited list of layer directories. For each directory in this list, a `build/conf/layer.conf` file is searched for and parsed with the `LAYERDIR` variable being set to the directory where the layer was found. This process automatically sets up `BBPATH` and other variables for a given build directory for the user.

> The order of the listed layers in the `BBLAYERS` variable is followed by BitBake when parsing the metadata. In case your layer needs to be parsed first, be sure to have it listed in the right order in `BBLAYERS`.

BitBake then expects to find `meta/conf/bitbake.conf` in the user-specified `BBPATH`. The configuration file generally has the `include` directives to pull in many other metadata such as architecture specific ones, machine configuration files, and the `build/conf/local.conf` file. Only variable definitions and the `include` directives are allowed in configuration files (`.conf`). BitBake's classes (`.bbclass`), as said earlier, are its rudimentary inheritance mechanism. They're parsed when an `inherit` directive is encountered, and they are located in `classes/`, relative to the directories in `BBPATH`.

A BitBake recipe (`.bb`) is a logical unit of tasks to be executed. Normally, this is a package to be built. Inter-recipe dependencies are obeyed. The files themselves are found via the `BBFILES` variable, which is set to a space separated list of the `.bb` files, and handles wildcards.

Dependencies

In order to accomplish the dependency, the recipes must declare what they need to have available during the build process. BitBake ensures that the build-time dependencies are satisfied before starting the recipe build. This is easier to understand if we think about an application that uses a library. So, this library must be built and its headers made available for use, before the application itself can be built. The `DEPENDS` variable is used in a recipe to inform BitBake about the build-time dependency.

When an application depends on something to run, this is called a runtime dependency. This is common for shared data among applications (for example, icons), which is used only when running the application but not used during its build process or when an application calls another during its execution. The runtime dependencies can be expressed using the `RDEPENDS` variable in a recipe.

With the recipe dependencies chain, BitBake can sort all the recipes in a feasible order for the build. This permits BitBake to organize tasks in the following ways:

- Recipes that do not have a dependency relation are built in parallel
- Dependent recipes are built in a serial order, sorted in a way the dependencies are satisfied

 Every recipe included in the runtime dependencies is put in the build list. This sounds obvious, but even though they are not used during the build, they are included because they need to be ready for use so that the resulting binary packages are installable.

Preferring and providing recipes

The dependency relation between recipes is core to BitBake and the build tool as a whole. It is defined inside each recipe file, with a variable which describes on what a recipe depends (DEPENDS) and what a recipe provides to the system (PROVIDES). These two variables together build the dependency graph used by BitBake during the dependency resolution.

So, if a recipe foo_1.0.bb depends on bar, BitBake lists all recipes providing bar. The bar dependency can be satisfied by the following:

- The bar_<version>.bb format as every recipe provides itself
- A recipe with the PROVIDES variable set to bar

A dependency can be satisfied by several recipes (for example, two or more recipes have PROVIDES += "bar"). In this case, we must inform BitBake the provider to use.

The virtual/kernel provider is a clear example where this mechanism is used. The virtual/ namespace is the convention adopted when we have a set of commonly overridden providers.

All recipes that require the kernel to build can add virtual/kernel to the dependency list (DEPENDS), and BitBake makes sure to satisfy the dependency. When we have more than one recipe with an alternative provider, we must choose one to be used, for example, PREFERRED_PROVIDER_virtual/kernel = "linux-mymachine".

The virtual/kernel provider is commonly set in the machine definition file as it may vary from one machine to another. We see how to create a machine definition file in *Chapter 11, Creating Custom Layers*.

When BitBake cannot satisfy a dependency, due to a missing provider for it, an error is raised.

The preference cannot be set per recipe; so, in the same system, two recipes cannot use different providers for the same dependency.

When BitBake has two providers with different versions, it uses the higher version by default. We can force BitBake to use a different version by using `PREFERRED_VERSION`. This is commonly found in BSPs, such as bootloaders, where vendors use different versions depending on the board.

When we have a development or an unreliable version of a recipe, and we do not want it to be used by default, we can use `DEFAULT_PREFERENCE = "-1"` in the recipe file. So, even if the version is greater, it is not taken without it being explicitly set (using `PREFERRED_VERSION` for it).

Fetching the source code

One of the main features supported by BitBake is source code fetching. This support has been designed to be as modular and as flexible as possible. The mechanism used by BitBake to fetch the source code is internally called as **fetcher backend**. There are several fetcher backends supported, which can be configured to align the user requirements and optimize source code fetching.

When the Poky source code is downloaded, what is actually copied is the metadata and the BitBake tool. All other source code is fetched on demand. Every Linux-based system includes the Linux kernel and several other utilities that form the root filesystem, such as `openssh`. The OpenSSH source code is available from its upstream website as a `tar.gz` file hosted on a FTP server; the Linux kernel release may be fetched from a **Git** repository.

BitBake offers support for many different fetcher modules that allow retrieval of tarball files and a number of other protocols such as Git, Subversion, Bazaar, OSC, HTTP, HTTPS, FTP, CVS, Mercurial, Perforce, or SSH.

Remote file downloads

BitBake supports several methods for remote file downloads. The most commonly used are `http://`, `https://`, and `ftp://`. We won't cover the internal details of how BitBake handles it but focus on the visible effects of it.

When BitBake executes the `do_fetch` task in a recipe, it checks the `SRC_URI` contents. If we look at, for example, the `libjson` recipe (available at `meta/recipes-devtools/libjson/libjson_0.9.bb`), the processed variables are the following:

```
SRC_URI = "http://oss.metaparadigm.com/json-c/json-c-${PV}.tar.gz"
SRC_URI[md5sum] = "3a13d26...de24abae"
SRC_URI[sha256sum] = "702a486...39439475"
```

BitBake expands the `PV` variable to the package version, `0.9` in this example, downloads the file from the URL `http://oss.metaparadigm.com/json-c/json-c-0.9.tar.gz`, and then saves it at the path pointed out by the `DL_DIR` variable. After the download is complete, BitBake compares the `md5sum` and `sha256sum` values of the downloaded file with the values from recipe, and if both values match, it creates a `${DL_DIR}/json-c-0.9.tar.gz.done` file to mark the file as successfully downloaded and checked. This way, when BitBake looks for the file next time, it knows that it can safely be reused, and it skips the file's `checksum` verification. This process happens for every remote file that BitBake downloads.

> By default, the `DL_DIR` variable points to `build/downloads`. You can override this using the `build/conf/local.conf` file as:
>
> ```
> DL_DIR = "/my/download-cache"
> ```
>
> This makes it easy to share the same download cache among several different build directories, thus saving time and bandwidth.

Git repositories

One of the most commonly used source control management systems in use is Git. BitBake has a solid support for it, and the Git backend is used when the `do_fetch` task is run and finds a `git://` URL at the `SRC_URI` variable.

The default way for the BitBake's Git backend to handle the repositories is to clone the repository into `${DL_DIR}/git2/<git URL>`. For example, check the following quote from the `linux-firmware_git.bb` recipe found in `meta/recipes-kernel/linux-firmware/linux-firmware_git.bb` inside Poky:

```
SRCREV = "600caefd83a406540b2a789be6415e44c9b87add"

...

SRC_URI =
"git://git.kernel.org/pub/scm/linux/kernel/git/firmware/linux-
firmware.git"
```

Here, the `linux-firmware.git` repository is cloned into `${DL_DIR}/git2/git.
kernel.org.pub.scm.linux.kernel.git.firmware.linux-firmware.git`.

This directory name is chosen to avoid conflicts between other possible Git repositories with the same project name. The `SRCREV` variable is used by the `do_fetch` task to ensure the repository has the needed Git revision and forces an update in case it does not; it's used by the `do_unpack` task to set up the work directory in the wanted source revision.

> When the `SRCREV` variable points to a hash not available in the master branch, we need to use the `branch=<branch name>` parameter, as follows:
>
> ```
> SRC_URI = "git://myserver/myrepo.git;branch=mybranch"
> ```
>
> In the cases when the hash used points to a tag, which is not available in a branch, we need to use the `nobranch=1` option as the following:
>
> ```
> SRC_URI = "git://myserver/myrepo.git;nobranch=1"
> ```

Other repositories

The remote file and the Git repository are the most commonly used fetch backends of BitBake. The other source code management supports vary in the implementation, but the general ideas and concepts are the same.

Optimizing the source code download

To improve the robustness of source code download, Poky provides the mirror mechanism that can be configured in order to do the following:

- Provide a centrally preferred server for download
- Provide fallback servers

In order to provide this robust download mechanism, BitBake follows some steps. During the build, the first BitBake step is to search for the source code within the local download directory (pointed by `DL_DIR`). In case of failure, the next step is to try locations defined by the `PREMIRRORS` variable. In a recurrent case of failure, it searches the locations pointed out in the `MIRRORS` variable.

The following sections explain the PREMIRRORS and MIRRORS variables:

- PREMIRRORS: The second step in the download mechanism performed by BitBake is controlled by the variable PREMIRROR. For example, the Poky distribution sets it as the following:

```
PREMIRRORS_prepend = "\
    git://.*/.* http://www.yoctoproject.org/sources/ \n \
    ftp://.*/.* http://www.yoctoproject.org/sources/ \n \
    http://.*/.* http://www.yoctoproject.org/sources/ \n \
    https://.*/.* http://www.yoctoproject.org/sources/ \n"
```

  The preceding code prepends the PREMIRROR variable to change and instruct the build system to intercept any Git, FTP, HTTP, and HTTPS requests, and it redirects them to the http://www.yoctoproject.org/sources/ sources mirror.

  In case the desired component is not available in the source mirror, BitBake falls back to the MIRRORS variable.

- MIRRORS: The variable MIRRORS provides a set of alternative URL addresses for some servers where the source component may be found. BitBake tries one after another, and if all available mirrors fail, it raises an error.

We can take advantage of this download mechanism to save the download time by providing a local pull directory or a local network server by adding the following code to build/conf/local.conf:

```
SOURCE_MIRROR_URL ?= "file:///home/you/your-download-dir/"
INHERIT += "own-mirrors"
```

Here, SOURCE_MIRROR_URL can point to a local directory or to any server URL with the supported fetcher backend.

> In case the goal is to have a shareable download cache, it is advisable to enable the tarball generation for the SCM backends (for example, Git) in the download folder with BB_GENERATE_MIRROR_TARBALLS = "1" in build/conf/local.conf.

Disabling network access

Sometimes, we need to ensure that we don't connect to the Internet during the build process. There are several valid reasons for this, such as the following:

- **Policy**: Our company does not allow external source to be included in a product without a proper legal validation and review

- **Network cost**: When we are on the road using a mobile broadband, the cost of data may be too expensive as the data to download may be big

- **Build speed**: When we are sure we have already downloaded the required source code, we can turn off the network access in order to speed up the building process. This setup is commonly used in autobuild servers

- **Lack of network access**: Sometimes, we do not have access to a network

In order to disable the network connection, we need to add the following code in the `build/conf/local.conf` file:

```
BB_NO_NETWORK = "1"
```

Understanding BitBake's tasks

BitBake uses execution units, which are in essence a set of clustered instructions that run in sequence. These units are known as **tasks**. There are many tasks being scheduled, executed, and checked by BitBake during every recipe build, provided by classes to form the framework that we use to build a recipe. Some are important to be understood as we often use, extend, implement, or replace them ourselves when writing a recipe.

Run the following command:

```
$: bitbake <recipe>
```

BitBake runs a set of scheduled tasks. When we wish to run a specific task, we can use the following command:

```
$: bitbake <recipe> -c <task>
```

To list the tasks defined for a recipe, we can use the following command:

```
$: bitbake <recipe> -c listtasks
```

We will briefly describe each of these here:

- do_fetch: The first step when building a recipe is fetching the needed source. This is done using the fetching backends feature we discussed previously in this chapter. It is important to point out that fetching a source or a file does not mean it is a remote source. In fact, every file needed during the recipe build must be fetched so that it is made available in the WORKDIR directory. We will learn more about the build directory and its contents in *Chapter 5*, *Detailing the Temporary Build Directory*.

  All downloaded content is stored in the download folder (the DL_DIR variable), so all external source code is cached to avoid redownloading it every time we need the same source.

- do_unpack: The natural subsequent task after the do_fetch task is do_unpack. It is responsible for unpacking source code or to check out the requested revision or branch, in case the referenced source uses a SCM system.

- do_patch: Once the source code has been properly unpacked, BitBake initiates the process of adapting the source code. This is done by the do_patch task. Every file fetched by do_fetch, with the .patch extension, is assumed to be a patch to be applied. This task applies the list of patches needed.

  The process of applying a patch uses the S variable, which points to the source code. The default value used for S is ${WORKDIR}/${PN}-${PV}, and it is used for the do_patch, do_configure, do_compile and do_install tasks.

- do_configure, do_compile, and do_install: The tasks do_configure, do_compile, and do_install are performed in this order. Some recipes may omit one task or another. It is important to note that the environment variables defined in the tasks are different from one task to another.

  The tasks vary a lot from one recipe to another. Poky provides a rich collection of predefined tasks in the classes, which ought to be used when possible. For example, when the Autotools class is inherited by a recipe, it provides a known implementation for the do_configure, do_compile and do_install tasks.

- do_package: The do_package task splits the files installed by the recipe into logical components such as debugging symbols, documentation, and libraries. The do_package task ensures that files are split up and packaged correctly. We will cover the packaging details in more depth in *Chapter 6*, *Assimilating Packaging Support*.

Extending tasks

When the task content does not satisfy our requirements, we replace it (providing our own implementation) or append it. As we learn more extensively when learning about the BitBake metadata syntax in *Chapter 7, Diving into BitBake Metadata*, the _ append and _prepend operators can be used to extend a task with extra content. The new content is concatenated in the original task. For example, to extend a do_install task, we can use the following code:

```
do_install_append() {
      # Do my commands
}
```

The mechanism using which we can extend existing recipes is covered in *Chapter 12, Customizing Existing Recipes*.

Generating a root filesystem image

One of the most common uses of Poky is the **rootfs image generation** (rootfs). The rootfs image should be seen as a ready-to-use root filesystem for a target. The image can be made up of one filesystem or may include other artifacts to be available during its generation as the Linux kernel, device tree, and bootloader binaries and other filesystems. The process to generate the image is composed of several steps, and its most common usages are the following:

1. Generate the rootfs directory.
2. Create the required files.
3. Wrap the final filesystem accordingly to the specific requirements (it may be a disk file with several partitions and contents).
4. Finally, compress it, if applicable.

All these steps are performed by subtasks of do_rootfs.

The rootfs is basically a directory with the desired packages installed (the package generation is covered in *Chapter 6, Assimilating Packaging Support*), with the needed tweaks applied just afterwards. The tweaks make minor adjustments applied in the rootfs contents; for example, when building a development image, rootfs is adjusted to allow us to log in with root without a password.

The list of packages to be installed into `rootfs` is defined by a union of packages listed by `IMAGE_INSTALL` and the packages included by `IMAGE_FEATURES`; the image customization is detailed in *Chapter 11, Creating Custom Layers*. Each image feature can include extra packages for installation, for example, `dev-pkgs` that installs development libraries and headers of all packages listed to be installed in `rootfs`.

The list of packages to be installed is now filtered by the variable `PACKAGE_EXCLUDE`, which lists the packages that should not be installed. The packages listed in `PACKAGE_EXCLUDE` are only excluded from the list of packages to be explicitly installed.

> Packages listed in `PACKAGE_EXCLUDE` are installed into `rootfs` if it is needed to satisfy a runtime dependency.

Having the final set of packages to install, the `do_rootfs` task can initiate the process of unpacking and configuring each package, and its required dependencies, into the `rootfs` directory. This is done using a package backend's (**DEB**, **IPK**, or **RPM**) specific set of subtasks as it actually uses the package management system using a local package feed to do this step. The package feed is explained in *Chapter 6, Assimilating Packaging Support*.

With the `rootfs` contents unpacked, the post installation scripts of the referred packages must run to avoid the penalty of running them during first boot. Some scripts may need to be run in the target to succeed, and there is no problem with that, except in the case we use the `read-only-rootfs` image feature. The post-installation script and the other variants of it are covered in *Chapter 6, Assimilating Packaging Support*.

> All the post-installation scripts must be successful in case of a read-only `rootfs` directory.

The `rootfs` optimization is then executed. A **prelink** process optimizes the dynamic linking of shared libraries to reduce startup time of executables; the **mklibs** process optimizes the size of the libraries removing the unused symbols.

Now, the directory is ready to generate the filesystem. `IMAGE_FSTYPES` lists the filesystem to be generated, for example, `EXT3` or `UBIFS`.

> After `do_rootfs` has completely finished, the generated image file is placed in `<build-dir>/tmp/deploy/image/<machine>/`.

The process to create our image and the possible values for `IMAGE_FEATURES` and `IMAGE_FSTYPES` are described in *Chapter 11, Creating Custom Layers*.

Summary

In this chapter, we learned the metadata concept, how recipes depend on each other, and how Poky deals with dependencies. We also got a better view of the behind-the-scenes tasks done by BitBake to download all the required source code, to store it in the build directory used to build and generate packages, as well as and how these packages fit into generated images.

In the next chapter, we will see the contents of the build directory after complete image generation and how BitBake uses it in the baking process, including the contents of the temporary build directory and its generated files.

5
Detailing the Temporary Build Directory

In this chapter, we will understand the contents of the temporary build directory after a complete image generation and see how BitBake uses it in the baking process. We will learn how some of these directories can assist our understanding when things do not work as expected, providing a valuable source of information.

Detailing the build directory

The build directory is a central information and artifact source for every Yocto Project's tool user. Its main directories are the following:

- `conf`: This has the configuration files we use to control Poky and BitBake. The first use of this directory was in *Chapter 2, Baking Our Poky-based System*. It stores configuration files such as `build/conf/local.conf` and `build/conf/bblayers.conf`.

- `downloads`: This stores the downloaded tarballs. It can be seen as the download cache and has been detailed in *Chapter 4, Grasping the BitBake Tool*.

- `sstate-cache`: This has the packaged data snapshots. It is a cache mainly used to speed up the build process. This folder is detailed in *Chapter 6, Assimilating Packaging Support*.

- `tmp`: This is a temporary build directory. It is very handy; we will understand it better in the following sections.

Constructing the build directory

The Yocto Project's tool inputs and outputs were already detailed in a high abstract level in the previous chapters. We already know that BitBake uses metadata to generate a set of artifacts, including images. Besides the generated artifacts, BitBake creates much more content during the process, which may be used in several ways, dependent upon our goals.

During the build process, BitBake performs several tasks and modifies the build directory. We can understand it better following the usual BitBake flow, as follows:

- **Fetching**: The first action realized by BitBake is to download the source code. This step modifies the build directory, including a new tarball inside the `build/download` directory.

- **Source preparation**: After the fetching of the source code is complete, it must be prepared for use. This may involve, for example, the unpacking of a tarball or a clone of a local cached Git directory (from the download cache). The source code is prepared in the `build/tmp/work` directory. When the source code is ready, the needed modifications are applied (for example, applying needed patches).

- **Configuration and building**: With the ready-to-use source code, the building process can start. It involves the configuration of build options (for example, `./configure`) and building (for example, `make`).

- **Installing**: The built artifacts are then installed (for example, `make install`) in a proper directory under `build/tmp/work/<...>/image`.

- **Wrapping the sysroot**: The libraries, headers, and other files that need to be shared for cross-compilation are copied (and sometimes modified) in `build/tmp/sysroot`.

- **Creating the package**: The packages are generated using the installed contents, splitting the files into subpackages and creating the packages (for example, RPM).

Exploring the temporary build directory

It is critical to understand the **temporary build directory** (`build/tmp`). The temporary build directory is created just after the start of a build, and it's especially important to help us to identify why something didn't behave as expected.

The contents of the `build/tmp` directory are shown in the following figure:

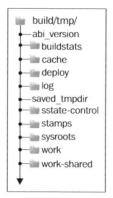

The most important directories found within it are the following:

- `deploy`: This contains the build products such as images, packages, and SDKs

- `sysroots`: This contains the shared libraries, headers, and utilities that are used in the process of building recipes

- `work`: This contains the working source code, a task's configuration, execution logs, and the contents of generated packages.

Understanding the work directory

The `build/tmp/work` directory is split by architecture. For example, when working with the machine `qemuarm`, we have the following four directories:

- `all-poky-linux`

- `armv5te-poky-linux-gnueabi`

- `qemuarm-poky-linux-gnueabi`

- `x86_64-linux`

The directories found here and their contents are architecture and machine dependent. We shouldn't take this as a final list, only as an illustration. The directory `x86_64-linux` is used to build the host `sysroot` content, which is detailed in the next section. The directory `all-poky-linux` holds the working build directories for the packages that are architecture agnostic. This fragmented structure is necessary to allow building multiple machines and architectures within one build directory without conflicting with each other.

The target machine we use is `qemuarm`. This machine is an emulation of the **ARM Versatile Platform Baseboard** with the ARM926EJ-S CPU emulation that supports the ARMv5TE instructions. Poky treats `qemuarm` as a type of ARMv5TE because some hardware features, may not be available in one device or another, even when they are supported by the CPU. Machine-specific recipes are built in the machine directory (`qemuarm-poky-linux-gnueabi` in this case) while the architecture-specific packages are built in the architecture-specific directory (`armv5te-poky-linux-gnueabi` in this case).

The `build/tmp/work` work directory is very useful when checking misbehavior or build failures. Its contents are stored in subdirectories following the pattern:

```
<arch>/<recipe name>/<software version>
```

Some of the directories under this tree are:

- `<sources>`: This is an extracted source code of the software to be built. This directory is pointed by the `WORKDIR` variable.
- `image`: This contains the files installed by the recipe (pointed by the `D` variable).
- `packages`: The extracted content of packages are stored here.
- `packages-split`: The content of packages, extracted and split, are stored here. This has a subdirectory for each package.
- `temp`: This stores BitBake's task code and execution logs.

The most commonly checked subdirectories are under the `sysroots` directory, which provides the artifacts used during cross-compilation as compilers, utilities, and libraries for the host and target; they are also checked under the `build/tmp/work` directory, which holds the working build directory. These directories provide valuable information for debugging.

> In order to reduce disk usage, we can automatically remove the work directory after each recipe compilation cycle, adding `INHERIT +=` `"rm_work"` in the `build/conf/local.conf` file.

The structure of the work directory is the same for all architectures. For every recipe, a directory with the recipe name is created. Taking the machine-specific work directory and using the `sysvinit-inittab` recipe as an example, we see the following:

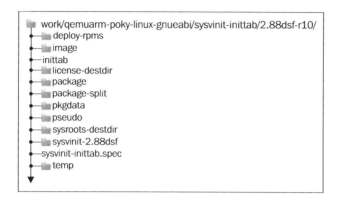

The `sysvinit-inittab` recipe is a good example, which even without a machine-specific object code is a machine-specific one. It contains the `inittab` file that defines, among other things, the serial console devices to spawn the login process, and this varies from machine to machine as the UART device depends on the machine schematic layout.

The directories shown in the preceding figure that are not detailed here are used by the build system.

You should not need to work with them, except if you are working on build tool development.

The work directory is very useful for debugging purposes; we cover this in *Chapter 9, Debugging with the Yocto Project*.

Understanding the sysroot directories

The content of the `sysroots` directory is shown in the following figure:

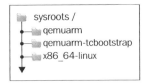

We can see three directories: `qemuarm`, `qemuarm-tcbootstrap`, and `x86_64-linux`.

The `qemuarm-tcbootstrap` directory is used as an intermediate directory for the compiler bootstrap as it needs some artifacts (for example, the `libc` headers), which is only useful for debugging if working on toolchain development.

The `x86_64-linux` directory is used (the name depends on the host machine architecture, for example, i686) to build host tools and libraries. The host `sysroot` is critical of the cross-compilation process as it provides the utilities used during the whole build process as `pkg-config`, `autotool`, `make`, `git`, and every other utility that is called during the build process; the binaries are built using the headers and libraries of the directory in order to isolate it completely from the GNU/Linux host distribution running in our development machine, and it is known as the host `sysroot`.

Our target machine (in our example, `qemuarm`) uses the `qemuarm` (target is `sysroot`) directory for headers and libraries required during the build. The utilities that must be run as part of the build process are called from the host `sysroot` so that both the `sysroot` directories play a core role in the cross-compiling process.

One common mistake to avoid, when designing a library recipe, is not getting its contents installed properly (the headers, static, and shared libraries) into the directory pointed by variable `D` so that Poky can, most of time, make the right installation of the needed files to `sysroot`. When we see a missing header or a link failure, we must double-check if our `sysroot` (target and host) contents are correct.

Summary

In this chapter, we explored the contents of the temporary build directory after a complete image generation, and saw how BitBake uses it along the baking process. We then learned how to use these directories for debugging.

In the next chapter, we will get a better understanding of how packaging is done in Poky, how to use package feeds and the PR service, and how they may help in our product maintenance.

6
Assimilating
Packaging Support

This chapter presents the key concepts to understand Poky and BitBake; it teaches us the concepts related to packaging. We will learn about the supported package formats, what **shared state cache** is and why it is needed, the package versioning components, how to set up and use **package feeds** to support our development process, and more.

Using supported package formats

The main goal of most of Poky's tasks is to produce packages. The other tasks use built packages to make other deliverables such as images and toolchains.

A recipe may generate one or more packages as a result of it being executed by BitBake; on the other hand, images and toolchains are made of several packages that are unpacked and configured to accomplish the intended goal. The generated result is wrapped in such a way that it can be installed into one or more images, or it can be deployed for later use.

List of supported package formats

Currently, BitBake supports four different package formats:

- **RPM**: Originally named **Red Hat Package Manager**, but now known as the RPM package format since its adoption to several other Linux distributions, it is used by several popular Linux distributions such as SuSE, OpenSuSE, Red Hat, Fedora, CentOS, among others.

- **DEB**: The **Debian Package Manager** is used by Debian and several other Debian-based distributions; the most widely known among them are Ubuntu Linux and Linux Mint.

- **IPK**: The **Itsy Package Management System** was a lightweight package management system designed for embedded devices that resembled Debian's package format. The initial project was discontinued, and the several embedded build systems and distributions that used it were moved to the **Opkg fork** made by **OpenMoko**; it is also used by the **OpenWrt** project. Currently, the OpenEmbedded-Core, and as a consequence Poky, uses the Opkg package manager to support the IPK format.

- **TAR**: This is derived from the tape archive .tar, and it is a widely used tarball file type used to group several files into only a single file.

Choosing a package format

The support for the formats is provided using a set of classes (package_rpm, package_deb, and package_ipk). We can select one or more formats using the PACKAGE_CLASSES variable, as shown in the following example:

```
PACKAGE_CLASSES ?= "package_rpm package_deb package_ipk"
```

This can be done, for example, in the build/conf/local.conf file. Using the PACKAGE_CLASSES variable, we can generate the packages in one or more formats.

> Images are created from the first package format found in PACKAGE_CLASSES.

Poky defaults to the RPM package format, which uses the smart package manager. However, the most adequate format depends on several aspects, including package format specific features, memory and resource usage, and so on. Another aspect is habit; for example, OpenEmbedded-Core users often feel more comfortable using IPK and opkg as the package manager as it is OpenEmbedded-Core's default and offers a smaller footprint in memory and resource usage. On the other hand, people used to Debian-based systems may prefer to use the APT and DEB package format for their products.

Running code during package installation

Packages can use scripts as part of their installation and removal process. The included scripts are defined as follows:

- `preinst`: This executes before the package is unpacked. Services should be stopped during the execution of `preinst` to permit the installation or upgrade.

- `postinst`: This typically completes any required configuration of the package after it has been unpacked. Many `postinst` scripts then execute any command necessary to start or restart a service once a new package has been installed or upgraded.

- `prerm`: This usually stops any daemon that is associated with a package. It is executed before the removal of files associated with the package.

- `postrm`: This commonly modifies links or other files created by the package.

The scripts are supposed to be run after the package installation (`postinst`) is run during the root filesystem creation. If the script returns a success value, the package is marked as *installed*. If the script execution returns an error, the package is marked as *unpacked*. All packages marked as unpacked have their scripts executed again immediately in the first boot of the image.

In order to add a `postinst` script, we can use the following code as example:

```
pkg_postinst_${PN} () {
#!/bin/sh -e
# Insert commands above
}
```

Instead of using the package name itself, we can use the variable `PN` that automatically expands the package name of the recipe.

To delay the script execution so that it runs on the target device itself (we should avoid this), we use the following structure in the post-installation script:

```
pkg_postinst_${PN} () {
#!/bin/sh -e
if [ x"$D" = "x" ]; then
    # Insert commands here
else
    exit 1
fi
}
```

In the previous example, we can see how the execution of the script is delayed. If the variable $D has a value, the script returns an error and the package is set as unpacked. It means that any command inserted in the conditional `if` section is executed only if the variable $D is unset.

We can also skip postscript execution, at the `rootfs` creation time, for example, to avoid trying to start a daemon at that time, but yet ensure that it is properly started when being upgraded in the device. Here is one example:

```
pkg_postinst_${PN} () {
#!/bin/sh -e
if [ x"$D" != "x" ]; then
    exit 0
fi
# Insert commands here to restart
}
```

When we generate an image with `read-only-rootfs` in IMAGE_FEATURES, all post-installation scripts must succeed. If any script returns an error and the package is set as unpacked only, forcing the script to be run after the root filesystem is created, the `do_rootfs` task fails. This check during build time ensures that we identify the problem while building the image rather than during the initial boot operation in the target device due to the impossibility of writing the filesystem.

> Make sure all the `pkg_postinst` script execution for installed packages is feasible during `do_rootfs`. This is required in case `read-only-rootfs` is in IMAGE_FEATURES.

It is important to highlight that one of the most common mistakes when creating post-installation scripts is the lack of the variable $D in front of absolute paths. This allows two possible uses of $D, ensuring paths are valid in both the host and target environments and checking to determine which environment is being used as a method to take appropriate actions.

Another common mistake is the attempt to run processes that are specific to or dependent on the target architecture. The easiest solution, in this case, is to postpone the script execution of the target.

Understanding shared state cache

The default behavior of Poky is to build everything from scratch unless BitBake determines that a recipe does not need to be rebuilt. The main advantage of building everything from scratch is that the final result is fresh and there is no risk of previous data causing problems. However, rebuilding everything requires computational time and resources.

The strategy to determine whether a recipe must be rebuilt is complex. Basically, BitBake tries to track as much information as possible about every task, variable, and code used in the build process. BitBake then generates a checksum for all involved information for every task.

Poky uses all this information provided by BitBake to store snapshots of those tasks as a set of packaged data generating a cache, which is called **shared state cache** (sstate-cache). This cache wraps the contents of each task output in packages stored in the SSTATE_DIR directory. Whenever BitBake prepares to run a task, it first checks the existence of a sstate-cache package that matches. If the package is present, BitBake uses the prebuild built package.

This is a very simple view of the whole shared state mechanism, which is quite a complex piece of code. For an advanced overview, it is advised to read the *Shared State Cache* section of the *Yocto Project Reference Manual*.

When using Poky for several builds, we must bear in mind that sstate-cache needs to be cleaned from time to time since it keeps growing as more and more cached data is added for every build. There is an easy way of cleaning it, as follows:

```
$: ./scripts/sstate-cache-management.sh --remove-duplicated -d --
cache-dir=<path to sstate-cached>
```

This removes the duplicated and old data from the cache.

> When we need to rebuild from scratch, we either remove the build/tmp so that we can use sstate-cache to speed up the build or we remove both build/tmp and sstate-cache so that no cache is reused during the build.

Explaining package versioning

Package versioning is used to differentiate the same package in different stages of its lifecycle. From Poky's perspective, it is also used as part of the equation that generates the checksum used by BitBake to verify whether a task must be rebuilt.

The package version, also known as PV, plays a central role when we select which recipe to build. The default behavior of Poky is to always prefer the newest recipe version, unless there is an explicit different preference, as we discussed in *Chapter 4, Grasping the BitBake Tool*. For example, consider that we have two versions of the recipe myrecipe—myrecipe_1.0.bb and myrecipe_1.1.bb. BitBake, by default, builds the recipe with version 1.1.

Inside the recipe, we may have other variables that compose package versioning with the PV variable. These are package epoch, known as PE and package revision, known as PR.

The PE variable has a default value of zero and is used when the package version schema is changed, breaking the possibility of usual ordering. The epoch is prepended in the package version, forcing a higher number when needed. For example, if a package uses the date to compose the PV variables such as 20140101 and 20140201, the version schema is changed for a reason, and a new version 1.0 is released, it is impossible to determine whether version 1.0 is higher than version 20140201. So, PE = "1" is used, forcing the version 1.0 to be higher than 20140201 since 1:1.0 is greater than 0:20140101.

The PR variable has a default value of r0 and is used as part of package versioning. When it is updated, it forces BitBake to rebuild all tasks of a specific recipe. We can update it manually in the recipe metadata to force a rebuild we know is needed. Although the approach of manually setting the PR variables inside recipes may seem attractive, it is very fragile because it relies on human interaction and knowledge when it is required. Since Yocto Project 1.5, called **Dora**, BitBake uses the task checksums to control what needs to be rebuilt, and the manual PR increment is only used in extremely rare cases when the task checksum does not change.

In the next section, we will get a better understanding of how PR are handled nowadays, using the PR service.

Package feeds

As we discussed in *Chapter 4*, *Grasping the BitBake Tool*, the packages play a central role as images and SDKs rely on them. In fact, `do_rootfs` uses a local package repository to fetch. This repository is known as **package feed**.

There is no reason for this repository to be used just for the images or SDK build steps. In fact, there are several valid reasons to make this repository remotely accessible internally in our development environment or publically for use in the field. Some of these reasons are listed, including the following:

- Easy testing of an updated application during development stage, without the need of a complete system reinstallation
- Make additional packages more flexible so that they can be installed in a running image
- Update products in the field

To produce a solid package feed, we must ensure that we have consistent increments in the package revision every time the package is changed. It is almost impossible to do this manually, and the Yocto Project has a service, the PR service, specially designed to help in this area.

PR service, which is part of BitBake, is used in order to increment the PR without human interaction every time BitBake detects a checksum change in a task. Essentially, it injects a suffix in `PR` in the format `${PR}.X`. For example, considering `PR = "r34"` after subsequent PR service interactions, the `PR` value becomes `r34.1`, `r34.2`, `r34.3`, and so on.

When using Poky to generate images and not targeting a remote package feed, PR service is not required because BitBake triggers the needed rebuilds due to the task checksum changes. The use of PR service is critical for solid package feeds, as it requires the version increase in a linear fashion.

 Even though we ought to use PR service to have a solid package versioning, it does not exclude the need of setting `PR` manually in exceptional cases.

By default, PR service is not enabled or running. To enable it to run locally, we must set the `PRSERV_HOST` variable in the BitBake configuration, for example, in `build/conf/local.conf` as the following:

```
PRSERV_HOST = "localhost:0"
```

This approach is adequate when the build happens in a single computer, which builds every package of the package feed. BitBake starts and stops the server at each build and increases the needed PR values automatically.

For a more complex setup, with multiple computers working against a common, shared package feed, we must have a single PR service running, which is used by all building systems associated with the package feed. In this case, we need to start PR service in the server using the `bitbake-prserv` command, as shown:

```
$: bitbake-prserv ⬚⬚host <ip> ⬚⬚port <port> ⬚⬚start
```

In addition to hand-starting the service, we need to update the BitBake configuration (for example, `build/conf/local.conf`) file of each build system, which connects to server using the `PRSERV_HOST` variable as described earlier so that each system points to the server IP and port.

Using package feeds

In order to use package feeds, the following two components have to be configured properly:

- The server, to provide access to the packages
- The client, to access the server and download the needed packages

The set of packages offered by the package feed is determined by the recipes we build. We can build one or more recipes and offer them, or we can build a set of images to generate the desired packages. Once we are satisfied with the amount of packages offered, we must create the index of packages to be provided by the package feeds. It is performed by the following command line:

```
$: bitbake package-index
```

The package index, along with the packages, must be made available through a transfer protocol such as HTTP. We can use any server we wish for this task, such as Apache, Nginx, Lighttpd, and others.

We need to configure the build system to make the runtime package manager, which is installed in the image, to point to the package feed server. This is done using the variable `PACKAGE_FEED_URIS` added in the BitBake configuration (that is, `build/conf/local.conf`), similar to the following example:

```
PACKAGE_FEED_URIS = "http://myfeedserver/repo/"
```

In addition, our image should have the `package-management` feature in `IMAGE_FEATURES` to ensure that when the image is created for our target, it includes the package databases and the target-specific tools for runtime package management to be available on the target. We detail the variable `IMAGE_FEATURES` in *Chapter 11, Creating Custom Layers*.

 In case we want a small image with no package management support, we should not include `package-management` in `IMAGE_FEATURES`.

The `PACKAGE_FEED_URIS` and `IMAGE_FEATURES` configurations guarantee that the image running in the client side can access the server and has the needed utilities in order to install, remove, and upgrade its packages.

After these steps have been taken, we are able to use the runtime package management in target. For example, if we choose the `RPM` package format for the image, we can fetch the repository information using the following command:

```
$: smart update
```

Use the `smart query` and `smart install` commands to find and install packages from the repositories.

The use of package feeds to upgrade the product is a great solution. However, it must be reliable. Our development process must be very careful and test all different possible upgrade scenarios in order to avoid bad surprises.

Summary

This chapter presented to us the basic concepts of packaging, a concept that has a central role for Poky and BitBake, package versioning, and how this impacts Poky's behavior when rebuilding packages and package feeds. It also showed us how to configure an image to be updated using prebuilt packages provided by a remote server.

In the next chapter, we will learn about the BitBake metadata syntax and its operators to `append`, `prepend`, and `remove` content from variables, variable expansions, and so on. We will then be able to understand the language used in the Yocto Project engines better.

7
Diving into BitBake Metadata

At this point, we know how to generate images and packages and use package feeds, which is basically everything we must know for simple usage of Poky. Hereafter, we will learn how to control the behavior of Poky to accomplish our goals and take maximum benefit from the Yocto Project as a whole.

In this chapter, we will enhance our understanding of the BitBake metadata syntax. We will learn to use the `append`, `prepend`, and `remove` operators to alter content from variables, variable expansions, and so on. These are the key concepts we can use to make our own recipes and customizations that we will learn about in *Chapter 10, Exploring External Layers*, *Chapter 11, Creating Custom Layers*, and *Chapter 12, Customizing Existing Recipes*.

Using metadata

The amount of metadata used by BitBake is enormous. To take the maximum profit out of using Poky, we must master it. As we learned in *Chapter 4, Grasping the BitBake Tool*, metadata can be classified into the following three major areas:

- **Configuration** (the `.conf` files): Configuration files define the global content that is used to provide information and configure how the classes and recipes will work

- **Classes** (the `.bbclass` files): Classes are available to the whole system and can be inherited by recipes to easily maintain and avoid code duplication while the recipes describe the tasks to be run and provide the needed information to allow BitBake to generate the needed task chain

- **Recipes** (the `.bb` or `.bbappend` files): Recipes and classes are written in a mix of Python and Shell Scripting code

Working with metadata

The syntax used by BitBake metadata may be misleading, which can sometimes be hard to trace. We can check the value of each variable we want using the environment option (-e or --environment) of BitBake, for example:

```
$: bitbake -e <recipe> | grep <variable>
```

In order to understand how BitBake works in more detail, please refer to the *BitBake User Manual*.

In the following sections, we will see most of the syntaxes commonly used in recipes.

The basic variable setting

The assignment of a variable can be done as shown:

```
FOO = "bar"
```

In the preceding example, the value of the variable FOO is bar.

The variable assignment is core to the BitBake metadata syntax as most other examples are performed using variables.

Variable expansion

BitBake supports variable referencing. The syntax closely resembles Shell Script, for example:

```
A = "aval"
B = "pre${A}post"
```

This results in A containing aval and B containing preavalpost. One important thing to bear in mind is that the variable only expands when it is actually used, as shown:

```
A = "aval"
B = "pre${A}post"
A = "change"
```

The preceding example illustrates the *laziness* of BitBake evaluation. When B is used, it evaluates A (as it is a reference for it), A now contains change, and B is prechangepost.

Setting a default value using ?=

When there is a need to provide a default value, the operator ?= can be used. The following code shows its use:

```
A ?= "aval"
```

If A is set before the preceding code is called, it retains its previous value; if A has not been previously set, it is set to aval. Basically, the ?= operator assigns a new value to a variable if one has not already been set.

Note that, if there are multiple ?= assignments to a single variable, the first of these is used. For example, in case we have the following:

```
A ?= "aval"
A ?= "change"
```

The variable A has the value aval. However, if we have A previously set, then it is used. For example:

```
A = "before"
A ?= "aval"
A ?= "change"
```

The A variable is kept as before.

Setting a default value using ??=

Another way to provide a default value is using the ??= operator. The difference between ??= and ?= is that with ??= the assignment does not occur until the end of the parsing process, so that the *last* rather than the *first* ??= assignment to a given variable is used. Check the following code:

```
A ??= "somevalue"
A ??= "someothervalue"
```

If A is set before the preceding code, it retains the value. If A has not been previously set, it is set to someothervalue.

Immediate variable expansion

Use the := operator when there is a need to force immediate expansion of a variable. It results in the variable's contents being expanded immediately rather than when the variable is actually used, as follows:

```
T = "123"
A := "${B} ${A} test ${T}"
```

```
B = "${T} bval"
T = "456"
C = "cval"
C := "${C}append"
```

At the end of this example, A will contain `test 123`, B will contain `456 bval`, and C will be `cvalappend`. When A is expanded, B is not yet defined, so B is empty.

Appending and prepending

BitBake offers two sets of appending and prepending operators. The first are `+=` and `=+`. The following code illustrates their use:

```
B = "bval"
B += "additionaldata"
C = "cval"C =+ "test"
```

At the end of this example, B contains `bval additionaldata` and C contains `test cval`. It is important to note that these operators *include* an extra space between each call. When we wish to avoid adding spaces, we use the `.=` and `=.` operators. Look at the following code:

```
B = "bval"
B .= "additionaldata"
C = "cval"
C =. "test"
```

In this example, B is now `bvaladditionaldata` and C is `testcval`. In contrast to the preceding example, the `.=` and `=.` operators add *no* additional space. Commonly, the `+=` and `=+` operators are used to add items to lists while the `.=` and `=.` operators are used to concatenate strings.

To concatenate strings, we can also use the `append` and `prepend` operators, as shown:

```
B = "bval"
B_append "additionaldata"
C = "cval"
C_prepend "test"
```

In this example, B is now `bvaladditionaldata` and C is `testcval`. These operators add no additional space.

Conditional metadata set

BitBake provides a very easy-to-use way to write conditional metadata. It is done by a mechanism called **overrides**.

The variable OVERRIDES contains values separated by colons (:), and each value is an item we want to satisfy conditions. So, if we have a variable that is conditional on arm, and arm is in OVERRIDES, then the version of the variable that is specific to arm is used rather than the nonconditional version, as shown:

```
OVERRIDES = "architecture:os:machine"
TEST = "defaultvalue"
TEST_os = "osspecificvalue"
TEST_condnotinoverrides = "othercondvalue"
```

In this example, TEST will be osspecificvalue due to the condition of os being in OVERRIDES.

Conditional appending

BitBake also supports appending and prepending to variables based on whether something is in OVERRIDES, as shown:

```
DEPENDS = "glibc ncurses"
OVERRIDES = "machine:local"
DEPENDS_append_machine = " libmad"
```

In the preceding example, DEPENDS is set to glibc ncurses libmad.

File inclusion

BitBake provides two directives for file inclusion: include and require.

With the first directive, include, BitBake attempts to insert the file at that location. If the path specified on the include line is a relative path, BitBake locates the first instance it can find within BBPATH. If the referenced file cannot be found, the parsing does not fail.

By contrast, the second directive, require, raises ParseError if the file to be included cannot be found. In all other respects, it behaves just like the include directive.

The convention normally adopted in the Yocto Project is to use a .inc file to share common code between two or more recipe files.

Python variable expansion

BitBake makes it easy to use Python code in variable expansion with the following syntax:

```
VARIABLE = "${@<python-command>}"
```

This gives huge flexibility to the user, as can be seen in the following example:

```
DATE = "${@time.strftime('%Y%m%d',time.gmtime())}"
```

This results in the DATE variable containing today's date.

Defining executable metadata

Metadata recipes (.bb) and class (.bbclass) files can use Shell Script code as follows:

```
do_mytask () {
    echo "Hello, world!"
}
```

This is essentially identical to setting a variable, except that this variable happens to be an executable shell code. It is important to be careful when writing Shell Script code as we should not use shell-specific code such as bash or zsh. When in doubt, a good way to test if our code is safe is to use the **dash shell** to test it.

Another way to inject code is by using Python code, as shown:

```
python do_printdate () {
    import time
    print time.strftime('%Y%m%d', time.gmtime())
}
```

This is similar to the previous code but flags it as Python so that BitBake knows it is Python code and runs it accordingly.

Defining Python functions in the global namespace

We may be required to use Python functions to generate the value for a variable or some other use. This can be easily done, in recipes (.bb) and classes (.bbclass), using the following code:

```
def get_depends(d):
    if d.getVar('SOMECONDITION', True):
```

```
        return "dependencywithcond"
    else:
        return "dependency"
SOMECONDITION = "1"
DEPENDS = "${@get_depends(d)}"
```

Usually, we need to access the BitBake database when writing a Python function. A convention among all metadata is that the d variable is used to point to the BitBake's database, and it is usually passed as the last parameter of a function.

So, in the preceding example, we ask the database the value of the SOMECONDITION variable and return a value depending on it.

The example results in DEPENDS containing dependencywithcond.

The inheritance system

The inherit directive is a means of specifying what classes of functionality our recipe (.bb) requires. It is a rudimentary form of inheritance. For example, we can easily abstract out the tasks involved in using autoconf and automake, and put that into .bbclass for our recipes to make use of it. A given .bbclass is located by searching for classes/filename.bbclass in BBPATH, where filename is what we inherited. So, in a recipe that uses autoconf or automake, we can use the following:

```
inherit autotools
```

This instructs BitBake to inherit autotools.bbclass, so it provides the default tasks that works fine for most autoconf or automake based projects.

Summary

In this chapter, we learned in detail about the BitBake metadata syntax; its operators to append, prepend, and remove content from variables; variable expansions; and so on, including some usage examples for them.

In the next chapter, we will learn how to use Poky to create external compilation tools and produce a root filesystem suitable for cross development. In addition, the possible use of **Eclipse** integration will be explained.

8

Developing with the Yocto Project

So far, we have used Poky as a build tool; in other words, we have used it as a tool to design and generate the image that will be used on products. In this chapter, we will understand how the tool can help us with application or kernel development, creating external compilation tools, producing a root filesystem suitable for cross development, and generating an image with the tools for use in the target machine for development.

Deciphering the software development kit

A **software development kit (SDK)** is a set of tools and files used to develop and debug. These tools include compilers, linkers, debuggers, external library headers, and binaries, and may include custom utilities and applications. This set of programming tools is called a **toolchain**.

In embedded development, the toolchain is often composed of cross-tools, or tools executed on one architecture that produces a binary for use in another architecture. For example, a gcc binary that runs on an x86-64-compatible machine and produces one binary for an ARM machine is a cross-compiler. When the tool and resultant binary are executed in the same architecture, it is called a native build.

Usually, when we work on a custom source code and use external libraries, for example, libusb or libgl, these libraries are used to build at runtime. The custom source may be built against the library header files, and the binary may be located somewhere during the execution. The set of files used during build time is placed under the sysroots directory, part of the Poky SDK, which is very configurable, depending on application, or it is a very simple one for general use.

When Poky executes tasks through the use of BitBake, it also needs a toolchain to be able to compile and link binaries for the target. This is called an internal toolchain because the tools are used internally by the build system. These tools are not intended to be used externally as they are not prepared for that, although they may be used on some very specific and advanced use cases.

Working with the Poky SDK

Usually, the standard Poky workflow includes creating an image and package recipes and deciding what will be installed on the final product image. However, a huge amount of time is spent developing, writing, testing, or adapting source code for our application.

So, when we write and test our application, we only care about the application itself, providing the libraries that the application requires precede application development, although this can be an iterative process. However, we want a test environment that looks as similar as possible to the final one, mainly because of the toolchain compatibility and also to avoid behavioral changes when we integrate the application into our product.

To help with this task, we can create a toolchain to be used externally with the Poky environment. Poky generates an SDK package that can be installed on any computer, independent of Poky being installed on it. In addition, the installed toolchain is compatible with the internal one. Besides the toolchain, the SDK can also provide a set of library files (such as library binaries and header files), depending on our needs.

Using an image-based SDK

For a custom source code, we know the dependency libraries and the other applications we depend on. In such cases, we can create an image that reflects exactly our needs or uses the closest image provided by Poky.

In order to create the image-based SDK, execute the following command:

```
$: bitbake core-image-full-cmdline -c populate_sdk
```

With this command, the SDK is created based on the `core-image-full-cmdline` image. If we have a custom image, we can use it instead. The SDK is generated following the architecture of `MACHINE` that we have set for.

After it being built, a binary script can be found at `build/tmp/deploy/sdk/poky-eglibc-x86_64-core-image-full-cmdline-armv5te-toolchain-1.6.sh`.

Do not open the preceding script on a simple text editor. The script has a piece of binary code that may cause a text editor to crash.

The resultant script should be installed before being used. We can see the installation process in the following screenshot:

```
⊗ ⊖ ☐  Installation of sdk from build/tmp/deploy
$: ./poky-eglibc-x86_64-core-image-full-cmdline-armv5te-toolchain-1.6.sh
Enter target directory for SDK (default: /opt/poky/1.6):
You are about to install the SDK to "/opt/poky/1.6". Proceed[Y/n]?y
[sudo] password for user:
Extracting SDK...done
Setting it up...done
SDK has been successfully set up and is ready to be used.
$:
```

In the preceding example, the installation directory was /opt/poky/1.6; however, we may choose any directory. The installation provides the following:

- environment-setup-armv5te-poky-linux-gnueabi: This is the script used to set up all environment variables needed to use the toolchain

- site-config-armv5te-poky-linux-gnueabi: This is the file with variables used during the toolchain creation

- version-armv5te-poky-linux-gnueabi: This is the version and timestamp information

- sysroots: This is a copy of the rootfs directory of images used for the SDK generation. It includes binary, header, and library files

- armv5te-poky-linux-gnueabi: This contains files for ARM machines

- x86_64-pokysdk-linux: These are files for machines with x86-64 compatibility

Generic SDK – meta-toolchain

Another option is to create a **generic SDK**, but with cross-compiler, debug tools, and a basic set of libraries and header files. This generic SDK is called **meta-toolchain**, and it is used mainly for kernel and bootloader development and the debug process. In order to create it, use the following command:

```
$: bitbake meta-toolchain
```

The resultant file is `build/tmp/deploy/sdk/poky-eglibc-x86_64-meta-toolchain-armv5te-toolchain-1.6.sh` for `qemuarm` machine. The installation process is exactly the same as the image-based SDK.

Although this SDK is very helpful, it is highly recommended to create a custom image that fits our application needs, and then create the SDK based on this.

Using a SDK

To use a SDK to build a custom application, for example, `hello-world.c`, we can use the following lines to build it, targeting the ARM architecture:

```
$: source /opt/poky/1.6/environment-setup-armv5te-poky-linux-gnueabi
$: ${CC} hello-world.c -o hello-world
```

In order to confirm that the generated binary was properly made for the target architecture, we can use the `file` utility as follows:

```
$: file hello-world

hello-world: ELF 32-bit LSB executable, ARM, EABI5 version 1
(SYSV), dynamically linked (uses shared libs), for GNU/Linux
2.6.16, BuildID[sha1]=1c92a9bb78448a848e88bafa8addf68d6f25460f,
not stripped
```

Another very commonly used project is the Linux kernel. The Linux kernel uses the LD utility for linking, so it is necessary to unset the LDFLAGS variable as it is, by default, defined for use with GCC. When we want to build the Linux kernel source code, we can use the following sequence of commands:

```
$: source /opt/poky/1.6/environment-setup-armv5te-poky-linux-gnueabi
$: unset LDFLAGS
$: make defconfig
$: make uImage
```

Developing applications on the target

For embedded systems, there is a debug portion that should be executed on real hardware because the application uses hardware-specific peripherals, and it may be difficult to emulate. In addition, some of the debug processes are dependent on source signals such as electric or optical, or the resultant action will be a mechanical behavior that may be difficult to test effectively on emulators.

The first proposed scenario for the development in target is to create a development image to be used along with an external toolchain. A development image is filled with header files and additional library links. This will be an image prepared to provide a build environment for a custom application, and it may be used with a custom toolchain or the Yocto Project external toolchain. The following line adds these properties to an image:

```
IMAGE_FEATURES += "dev-pkgs"
```

In case we want to modify only `build/conf/local.conf`, the variable to be used is `EXTRA_IMAGE_FEATURES`. The `IMAGE_FEATURES` variable is better described in *Chapter 11, Creating Custom Layers*.

The resulting image includes header files and additional library links, and it may be used during the custom application development cycle. The custom application may be built against this image root filesystem, which means that the image itself does not need to be recreated each time. In addition, the image may be shared among all developers working on the same project. Each one will have a copy, and everyone will be on the same page.

The `dev-pkgs` features install all `${PN}-dev` packages into the image.

For developers who prefer, or need, to use native build instead of creating a development build, Poky can be configured to generate an SDK image. This image contains the toolchain and development packages (header files and library links). It means we can have the source code of our custom application being built, run, tested, and debugged in the target machine.

In order to add the development tools inside an image, we need to include the `tools-sdk` feature in the `IMAGE_FEATURES` variable. We should use `EXTRA_IMAGE_FEATURES` if it is added in `build/conf/local.conf`.

The native build is preferred on newer microprocessors with more processing power and memory. It may be very slow on older microprocessors.

Integrating with Eclipse

Eclipse is a very powerful IDE and widely used for development and debugging on custom applications. It can be configured to work with Poky SDK. In the *Yocto Project Development Manual*, we find the supported Eclipse version and we learn how to configure it. Included with the manual are the Yocto Project ADT and an image based on generic toolchain integration.

As soon as our Eclipse is configured, we can use it for development. We can use the IDE to write the source code, and the Poky toolchain can be used to cross-compile it, as Eclipse supports the use of this external toolchain.

In addition, we can use Eclipse to deploy the generated binary file to the target, connected with Eclipse by Ethernet. The binary file and any other needed artifacts are copied to the target root filesystem, and it is possible to use it right after the transfer.

As soon as the binary is copied to the root filesystem, we can use Eclipse to debug the application. It means that we are allowed to use step-by-step debug, with the binary being run directly in the target machine.

In order to accomplish Eclipse integration, it's important to include the Eclipse feature in the target image by adding the following piece of code in `build/conf/local.conf`:

```
IMAGE_FEATURES += "eclipse-debug"
```

We, the authors, decided to not include a step-by-step on how to get Eclipse installed and configured because it requires several steps and will be outdated very fast. The *Yocto Project Development Manual*, on the other hand, gives a canonical place to find a complete and up-to-date tutorial for that.

Summary

In this chapter, we learned that the Yocto Project can be used for development as well as for image creation. We learned how to create two types of toolchains, image-based and generic, how to use them, and how to create a development image in order to build and deploy our application in the target. In addition, we learned how we can use Eclipse in the development phase to write, build, and debug our applications.

In the next chapter, we will understand how we can configure Poky to help us on the debugging process, how we can configure our system to provide the needed tools for a remote debug using GDB, how we can track our changes using `buildhistory`, and how we can use a handy tool called `devshell`.

9
Debugging with the Yocto Project

The debug process is an important step in every development cycle. In this chapter, we will understand how to configure Poky to help us with the debugging process, for example, how we can configure our system to provide the needed tools for a remote debug using GDB, how we can track our changes using `buildhistory`, and how we can use a handy tool called **devshell**.

Differentiating metadata and application debugging

When we first think about debugging, we usually don't realize that there are different types of debugging.

Metadata debugging is needed to ensure that the behavior of BitBake's tasks is aligned with our goals, and to identify the culprit, when it's not. In this case, we use several log files generated by BitBake in the host in order to help to trace the execution path of the involved task. As a consequence of a wrong behavior, a file may not be copied or a feature may not be enabled.

On the other hand, the debugging of run-time code is more natural for us as it is essentially the same as what we do during the normal development cycle of an application, a library, or a kernel. Depending on the kind of issue we are after, the right tool to help may vary from a debugger to code instrumentation (for example, adding debug prints).

In this chapter, we detail metadata debugging as it is the essence of the Yocto Project and supports us along the development and use of Poky.

Tracking image, package, and SDK contents

The easiest way to ensure we have the image, packages, and SDK, along with the expected contents, is to use the Build History mechanism. Its contents may change in unexpected ways when we change a recipe.

When a recipe is updated for a new version or has its code changed, it may influence the contents put in the generated packages and, as consequence, in the image or SDK.

As Poky deals with a huge amount of recipes, and our images or SDKs frequently have tens or hundreds of packages included, it may be quite difficult to track the package contents. The Poky tool responsible to help us in this task is the Build History.

The Build History, as we can guess from its name, keeps the history of contents of several artifacts built during the Poky use. It can track package, image, and SDK building.

To enable the Build History in our system, we need to add the following lines of code in our `local.conf` file:

```
INHERIT += "buildhistory"
BUILDHISTORY_COMMIT = "1"
```

The `INHERIT` method includes the `buildhistory` class hooks into the building process, while the `BUILDHISTORY_COMMIT` line enables BitBake to create a new Git commit in the `buildhistory` repository for every new package, image, or an SDK build. This makes the track as simple as `git diff` between two commits.

The data for all packages, images, and SDKs built is stored under the `build/buildhistory` directory as text files so that it is easy to use this data to extract extra information. Poky provides a utility that outputs the difference between two `buildhistory` states, called `buildhistory-diff`, in a more concise way, which is very useful when checking for changes.

The `buildhistory-diff` utility outputs the difference between any two Git revisions in a more meaningful way. We can see an example of its output in the following screenshot:

```
  ⊗ ⊖ ▢  buildhistory-diff output
$: ../sources/poky/scripts/buildhistory-diff
Changes to images/qemuarm/eglibc/core-image-minimal (files-in-image.txt):
  /usr/bin/strace was added
  /usr/bin/strace-log-merge was added
  * (installed-package-names.txt):
  *    strace was added
  *    * IMAGE_INSTALL: added "strace"
Changes to images/qemuarm/eglibc/core-image-minimal (installed-package-names.txt):
  strace was added
  * IMAGE_INSTALL: added "strace"
$:
```

The preceding screenshot shows the differences highlighted by `buildhistory-diff` when the package `strace` is added in the `core-image-minimal` image.

When a package is built, `buildhistory` creates a list of generated subpackages, installation scripts, a list of file ownership and sizes, the dependency relation, and more. For images and SDKs, the dependency relationship among the packages, filesystem files, and graph of dependency is created.

For a better understanding of all capabilities and features provided by the build history, you are advised to read the *Yocto Project Reference Manual*.

Debugging packaging

In more sophisticated recipes, we split the installed contents in several subpackages. The subpackages can be optional features, modules, or any other set of files that are optional to be installed.

To inspect how the recipe's content has been split, we can use the `build/tmp/work/<arch>/<recipe name>/<software version>/packages-split` directory. It contains a subdirectory for every subpackage and has its contents in the subtree. Among the possible reasons for a mistaken content split, we have the following:

- Contents not being installed (for example, an error in installation scripts)
- Application or library configuration error (for example, a disabled feature)
- Metadata error (for example, wrong package order)

Another common issue that we find, mainly in library recipes, is that the needed artifacts are not made available in the `sysroot` directory (for example, headers or dynamic libraries), causing a build breakage. The counterpart of the `sysroot` generation can be seen at `build/tmp/work/<arch>/<recipe name>/<software version>/sysroot-destdir`.

Other possible causes may need us to instrument the task code with the further presented logging functions, so we can figure out the logical error or bug that causes the unexpected result.

Logging information during task execution

The logging utilities provided by BitBake are very useful to trace the code execution path. BitBake provides logging functions for use in Python and Shell Script code, as described:

- **Python**: For use within Python functions, BitBake supports several log levels, which are `bb.fatal`, `bb.error`, `bb.warn`, `bb.note`, `bb.plain`, and `bb.debug`

- **Shell Script**: For use in Shell Script functions, the same set of log levels exists and is accessed with a similar syntax: `bbfatal`, `bberror`, `bbwarn`, `bbnote`, `bbplain`, and `bbdebug`

These logging functions are very similar to each other but have inner differences as described:

- `bb.fatal` and `bbfatal`: These have the highest priority of logging messages as they print the message and terminate the processing. They cause the build to be interrupted.

- `bb.error` and `bberror`: They are used to display an error but do not force the build to stop.

- `bb.warn` and `bbwarn`: They are used to warn users about something.

- `bb.note` and `bbnote`: These add a note to the user. They are only informative.

- `bb.plain` and `bbplain`: These output a message.

- `bb.debug` and `bbdebug`: These add debugging information that is shown depending on the debug level used.

There is one subtle difference between the use of the logging functions in Python and Shell Scripting.

The logging functions in Python are directly handled by BitBake, seen on the console, and stored in the execution log that can be seen inside `build/tmp/log/cooker/<machine>`.

When the logging functions are used in Shell Script, the information is outputted on the task's respective task log file, which is available in `build/tmp/work/<arch>/<recipe name>/<software version>/temp`.

Inside it, we can run the scripts for every task with the pattern `run.<task>.<pid>` and use the pattern `log.<task>.<pid>` for its output. For convenience, symbolic links are kept updated by BitBake, pointing to the last log files using the pattern `log.<task>`; thus, we can actually check for `log.do_compile`, for example, when intending to verify whether the right files were used during the build process. Alternatively, we can check for `log.do_patch` to verify whether a patch has been applied.

The `build/tmp/work` directory is detailed in *Chapter 5*, *Detailing the Temporary Build Directory*.

Utilizing a development shell

When editing packages or debugging build failures, **a development shell** can be a useful tool. When we use `devshell`, source files are extracted into the working directory, patches are applied, a new terminal is opened, and files are placed in the working directory.

In the new terminal, all the environment variables needed for the build are still defined, so we can use commands such as `configure` and `make`. The commands execute just as if the build system was executing them.

The following command is an example that uses `devshell` on a target named `linux-yocto`:

```
$: bitbake linux-yocto -c devshell
```

This allow us to rework the Linux kernel source code and build it in place, to avoid building it from scratch in our development machine, and change its code as needed.

 It is important to bear in mind that all changes made inside `devshell` are not persistent between builds; thus, we must be careful to record any change that is important, prior to leaving it.

As we have the source at our disposal, we can use it to generate extra patches. One very practical way of doing that is using Git and `git format-patch` to create the patch to be included in the recipe afterwards.

In order to include the generated patch in the recipe and make it persistent, see *Chapter 12*, *Customizing Existing Recipes*.

Using the GNU Project Debugger for debugging

While developing any project we, from time to time, end up struggling to understand subtle bugs. The **GNU Project Debugger (GDB)** is available as a package within Poky and is installed in SDK images by default, as was detailed in *Chapter 8*, *Developing with the Yocto Project*.

 In order to install debugging packages that contain the debug symbols and debugging tools in an image, add `IMAGE_FEATURES += "dbg-pkgs tools-debug"` in `local.conf`.

The use of the SDK, or an image with the debugging packages and tools installed, allows us to debug applications directly in the target, as we usually do in our development machine.

Sometimes, due to memory or disk space constraints, it is not possible to use GDB directly on the target to debug. These constraints arise because GDB needs to load the debugging information and the binaries of the process being debugged, and it needs to perform many computations to locate information such as function names, variable names and values, stack traces, and so forth even before starting the debugging process.

To overcome these constraints, we can use `gdbserver`, included by default when using `tools-debug` in `IMAGE_FEATURES`. It runs on the target and does not load any debugging information from the debugged process. Instead, a GDB instance processes the debugging information on the host. The host GDB then sends control commands to `gdbserver` to control the debugged application.

As the host GDB is responsible for loading the debugging information and performing the necessary processing to make the debugging process take place, the target does not need to have the debugging symbols installed and we need to make sure the host can access the binaries with their debugging information. It is advisable that the target binaries are compiled with no optimizations to facilitate the debugging process.

The process to use `gdbserver` and configure the host and target in the appropriate way is detailed in the *Yocto Project Development Manual*.

Summary

In this chapter, we understood how we can configure Poky to help us with the debugging process. We learned the contents of deployed directories that can be used on debugging, how we can track our changes using `buildhistory`, how we can use `devshell` to emulate the same build environment found by BitBake, and how we configure our system to provide the needed tools for GDB debugging.

In the next chapter, we will understand how to expand the Poky source code using external layers. We will be introduced to the concept of layering, and we will learn in detail the directory structure and the content of each layer type; additionally, we will learn how to add an external layer on our project manually or by using the Hob configuration.

10
Exploring External Layers

One of the most charming features of Poky is the flexibility of using external layers. In this chapter, we understand why this is a strong capability and how we can take advantage of this. We understand layer types and how their directory trees work. Finally, we learn how to include a new layer on our project or on a Hob configuration.

Powering flexibility with layers

Poky contains a great amount of metadata as machine definition files, classes, and recipes that cover everything from simple applications to full graphical stacks and frameworks. The main motivation to use layers is to organize the long list of providers better and still make sure users may be able to pick only the needed or desired provider. It is also a way to provide a customizable source code that can be used for any architecture or modified in the way the user needs.

We can choose the set of layers needed for each project. We can configure the provided source code for our needs because we want to configure how one package acts in our product or because we want the package built with our architecture flags. This means that using layers, we can provide additional features to Poky (represented by recipes from additional layers) that may be modified according to our needs (represented by the configuration appends we include for external recipes).

In addition, when creating our own custom project environment, instead of changing recipes and configuration files and appending files into one single layer, we ought to organize the metadata in different layers. The more separated the organization is, the easier it is to reuse the layers in future for other projects; for example, the Poky source code is separated in different layers. By default, it has three included layers as we can see on the output of the following command line:

```
$: bitbake-layers show-layers
```

The result can be seen in the following screenshot:

```
  ●  ─ ☐   included layers
$: bitbake-layers show-layers
                                                            priority
layer                      path
==================================================================
meta                       /home/user/yp/sources/poky/meta          5
meta-yocto                 /home/user/yp/sources/poky/meta-yocto     5
meta-yocto-bsp             /home/user/yp/sources/poky/meta-yocto-bsp 5
$: _
```

The command-line output shows the following three important properties of any layer:

- **Name**: This usually starts with the string `meta`.
- **Path**: This is important when we want to add an additional layer in our project being appended to the variable `BBPATH`.
- **Priority**: This is the value used by BitBake to decide which recipe to use and the order in which the `.bbappend` files should be joined. It means that if two layers include the same recipe file (`.bb`), the one with higher priority is used. In the `.bbappend` case, every `.bbappend` file is included in the original recipe, and the layer priority determines the order of inclusion so the `.bbappend` files within the highest priority layers are appended first, followed by the others.

Poky is arranged in three individual layers, coincidentally the three types available. The layer `meta` is the OpenEmbedded Core metadata, which contains the recipes, classes, and the QEMU machine configuration files. It is a software layer.

A **software layer** includes only applications or configuration files for applications and can be used on any architecture. There is a huge list of software layers. To name only a few, we have `meta-java`, `meta-qt5`, and `meta-browser`. The layer `meta-java` provides Java runtime and SDK support, the layer `meta-qt5` includes Qt5 support, and `meta-browser` supports several web browsers such as Firefox and Chrome.

The layer `meta-yocto-bsp` is the Poky reference **Board Support Package (BSP)** layer. It contains machine configuration files and recipes to configure packages for the machines. As it is a reference BSP layer, it can be used as an example.

The layer `meta-yocto` is the Poky reference **distribution layer**. It contains a distribution configuration used in Poky by default; this is an example of a distribution file. This default distro is described in the `poky.conf` file, and it is widely used for testing products. However, sometimes your product may have special needs and changes in `build/conf/local.conf` as required. The `build/conf/local.conf` file is a volatile file that is not supposed to be tracked by Git. We should not rely on it to set package versions, providers, and the system features for products, but use it just as a shortcut to test purposes during development.

The most adequate and maintainable solution is to create a distribution and a distribution layer to place the distro file into. This configuration allows any build to be reproduced afterwards. We can use one distribution layer for all distributions we have, or we can create one new layer for every new distribution; the better approach depends on your project needs.

> The policy configuration provided in a distribution layer overrides the same configuration from `build/conf/local.conf`.

Detailing the layer's source code

Usually, a layer has a directory tree, as shown in the following figure:

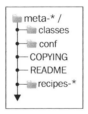

The layer name should start with `meta-`, it is not a requirement but the advised pattern. Inside this directory, there are two files, `<layer>/COPYING` and `<layer>/README`, a license, and a message to the user. In `<layer>/README`, we must specify any other dependency and information that the layer's users need to know.

The `classes` folder should hold the classes provided and specific to that layer (the `.bbclass` files). It is an optional directory.

The folder `<layer>/conf` is mandatory and should provide the configuration files (the `.conf` files). Primarily, the layer configuration file `<layer>/conf/layer.conf`, to be detailed in the next chapter, is the file with the layer definition.

When the `<layer>/conf` folder is from a BSP layer, the directory structure should look like the following figure:

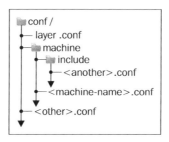

If the `<layer>/conf` folder is from a distribution layer, the directory structure should look like the following figure:

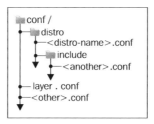

The `recipe-*` folder is a cluster of recipes separated by category, for example, `recipes-core`, `recipes-bsp`, `recipes-graphic`, `recipes-multimedia`, and `recipes-kernel`. Inside each folder starting with `recipes-`, there is a directory with the recipe name or a group of recipes; inside it, the recipe files end with `.bb` or `.bbappend`. For example, we can find the following resumed figure from `meta`:

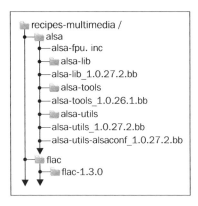

Adding meta layers

There are hundreds of meta layers from the Yocto Project, OpenEmbedded, communities, and companies that should be manually cloned inside the project source directory to be used. We can find them at `http://git.yoctoproject.org/` or `http://layers.openembedded.org`.

In order to include, for example, `meta-realtime` in our project, we can change the content of configuration for **Layers**; click on **Add layer**, browse to the `meta-realtime` folder, and click on **OK** if we use Hob, as shown in the following screenshot:

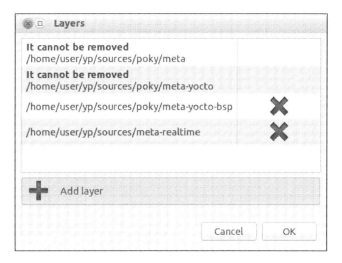

We notice that the layers `meta`, `meta-yocto`, and `meta-hob` cannot be removed as they provide the core infrastructure and BSP for Hob. These layers are the Yocto Project definition, plus the Hob provider layer.

If we use the BitBake command lines, we can add a new layer by changing the file `conf/bblayer.conf` and add the absolute path to the new meta layer directory, as shown in the following source code. The line highlighted is the one to be added. The others are the default values for this file.

```
conf/bblayer.conf's content
# LAYER_CONF_VERSION is increased each time build/conf/bblayers.conf
# changes incompatibly
LCONF_VERSION = "6"

BBPATH = "${TOPDIR}"
BBFILES ?= ""

#BBLAYERS ?= " \
#   /home/user/yp/sources/poky/meta \
#   /home/user/yp/sources/poky/meta-yocto \
#   /home/user/yp/sources/poky/meta-yocto-bsp \
#   "
BBLAYERS_NON_REMOVABLE ?= " \
   /home/user/yp/sources/poky/meta \
   /home/user/yp/sources/poky/meta-yocto \
   "

BBLAYERS += " \
   /home/user/yp/sources/meta-realtime \
   "
$: _
```

In the next BitBake command, or Hob launch, the added layer is parsed and the `meta-realtime` metadata is included in BitBake's database, allowing the packages inside the added layer to be used.

Summary

In this chapter, we introduced the concept of layering. We learned in detail the directory structure and the content of each layer type. In addition, we saw how to add an external layer on our project manually or by using the Hob configuration.

In the next chapter, we will learn more about why we need to create new layers and what is the common metadata included in them (such as machine definition files, recipes, and images), and wrap it all up with an example of distribution customization.

11
Creating Custom Layers

Beyond using existing layers from the community or from vendors, we learn why we create layers for our own products in this chapter. In addition, we understand how to create a machine definition and a distribution, and profit from them to better organize our source code.

Making a new layer

Before creating our own layer, it's always a good idea to check if there is a similar one already available in the OpenEmbedded metadata index (http://layers.openembedded.org). If we cannot find any suitable layer for our needs, the next step is to create the directory. Usually, the layer name starts with meta-, but this is not a technical restriction.

The layer configuration file is required in every layer and is placed in <layer>/conf/layer.conf; we can create it manually using any text editor or populate it with a script provided in Poky, as shown in the following command:

```
$: ./poky/scripts/yocto-layer create newlayer
```

The output is shown in the following screenshot:

```
creating a new layer meta-newlayer
$: cd sources/
$: ./poky/scripts/yocto-layer create newlayer
Please enter the layer priority you'd like to use for the layer: [default: 6]
Would you like to have an example recipe created? (y/n) [default: n] y
Please enter the name you'd like to use for your example recipe: [default: example]
Would you like to have an example bbappend file created? (y/n) [default: n] y
Please enter the name you'd like to use for your bbappend file: [default: example]
Please enter the version number you'd like to use for your bbappend file (this should
match the recipe you're appending to): [default: 0.1]

New layer created in meta-newlayer.

Don't forget to add it to your BBLAYERS (for details see meta-newlayer\README).
$: _
```

With the script, we are asked to enter the value for layer priority and answer other questions regarding the sample content that can be generated for the layer. We can use the default values or enter a custom one. An example of a generated layer is shown in the following figure:

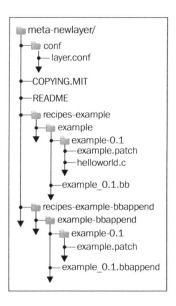

Important variables that we may need to add in case our layer requires other layers to work are as follows:

- LAYERVERSION: This is an optional variable that specifies the version of the layer in a single number. This variable is used within the LAYERDEPENDS variable in order to depend on a specific version of a layer, and it must be suffixed with the layer's name, for example, LAYERVERSION_newlayer = "1".

- LAYERDEPENDS: This lists the layers that the recipes depend upon, separated by spaces. Optionally, we can assign a specific layer version for a dependency by adding it to the end of the layer name with a colon, for example, otherlayer:2. This variable must be suffixed with the name of the specific layer, for example, LAYERDEPENDS_newlayer = "otherlayer".

If a dependency cannot be satisfied or the version numbers do not match, an error is raised. The base of the layer structure is now created and we see how to extend it in the following sections.

Adding metadata to the layer

The reasoning behind the use of layers is to add extra metadata to BitBake's database or change it.

The most commonly added features are project related, such as applications, libraries, or a service server.

On the other hand, instead of adding new features, it is much more usual to accommodate existing feature configurations to our needs, for example, the initial network values for a SSH server or the boot splash picture.

It means that we can include several types of metadata files on a new layer, recipes, images, and `bbappend` files to change existing features. The script used to create the new layer can, as well, create two example files; the first one, `example_0.1.bb` is a recipe example. The second one, `example_0.1.bbappend`, is a `bbappend` example used to modify the feature included by `example_0.1.bb`. There are several other examples of `bbappend` files on `meta-yocto-bsp` or `meta-yocto`, and we explore some of their common usages in the next chapter.

Creating an image

The image files can be seen as a set of packages grouped for a purpose and configured in a controlled way. We can create a new image, including an existing image, add the needed packages or override configurations; or we can create the image from scratch.

When an image mostly fits our needs and we need to do minor adjustments on it, it is very convenient to reuse its code. This makes code maintenance easier and highlights the functional differences. For example, if we want to include an application and remove an image feature, we can create an image at `recipes-my/images/my-image-sato.bb` with the following lines of code:

```
require recipes-sato/image/core-image-sato.bb
IMAGE_FEATURES_remove = "splash"
CORE_IMAGE_EXTRA_INSTALL += "myapp"
```

On the other hand, we sometimes want to create our image from scratch; we can facilitate our work using the `core-image` class as it provides a set of image features that can be used very easily, for example, an image in `recipes-my/images/my-image-nano.bb` consists of the following lines of code:

```
inherit core-image
IMAGE_FEATURES += "ssh-server-openssh splash"
CORE_IMAGE_EXTRA_INSTALL += "nano"
```

The append operator (+=) is used to guarantee that a new IMAGE_FEATURES variable can be added by build/conf/local.conf.

CORE_IMAGE_EXTRA_INSTALL is the variable we should use to include extra packages into the image when we inherit the core-image class that facilitates image creation, adding support for the IMAGE_FEATURES variable, which avoids a lot of duplication of code. The IMAGE_INSTALL variable groups the CORE_IMAGE_EXTRA_INSTALL contents, and IMAGE_FEATURES related packages generate our root filesystem.

Currently, the following are the image features supported:

- dbg-pkgs: This installs debug symbol packages for all packages installed in a given image.
- dev-pkgs: This installs development packages (headers and extra library links) for all packages installed in a given image.
- doc-pkgs: This installs documentation packages for all packages installed in a given image.
- nfs-server: This installs an NFS server.
- read-only-rootfs: This creates an image whose root filesystem is read-only.
- splash: This enables showing a splash screen during boot. By default, this screen is provided by **psplash**, which allows customization. If you prefer to use an alternative splash screen package, you can do so by setting the SPLASH variable to a different package name (or names) within the image recipe or at the distro configuration level.
- ssh-server-dropbear: This installs the **Dropbear** minimal SSH server that is used by default in case we use ssh-server, as it offers a smaller footprint and most of the OpenSSH features.
- ssh-server-openssh: This installs the OpenSSH SSH server, which is more full-featured than Dropbear. Note that if both the OpenSSH SSH server and the Dropbear minimal SSH server are present in IMAGE_FEATURES, then OpenSSH will take precedence and Dropbear will not be installed.
- staticdev-pkgs: This installs static development packages (that is, static libraries containing the *.a files) for all packages installed in a given image.
- tools-debug: This installs debugging tools such as strace and gdb.
- tools-profile: This installs profiling tools such as oprofile, exmap, and LTTng.

- `tools-sdk`: This installs a full SDK that runs on the device.

- `tools-testapps`: This installs device testing tools (for example, touchscreen debugging).

- `x11`: This installs the **X server**.

- `x11-base`: This installs the X server with a minimal environment.

- `x11-sato`: This installs the **OpenedHand Sato** environment.

Adding a package recipe

A package recipe is how we can instruct BitBake to fetch, unpack, compile, and install our application, kernel module, or any software provided by a project. Poky includes several classes that abstract the process for the most common development tools as projects based on **Autotools**, **CMake**, and **QMake**. A list of classes included in Poky can be seen in the *Yocto Project Reference Manual*.

One simple recipe that does the compile and install tasks explicitly is provided as follows:

```
DESCRIPTION = "Simple helloworld application"
SECTION = "examples"
LICENSE = "MIT"
LIC_FILES_CHKSUM = "file://${COMMON_LICENSE_DIR}/MIT;md5=0835ade698e0b
cf8506ecda2f7b4f302"

SRC_URI = "file://helloworld.c"

S = "${WORKDIR}"

do_compile() {
        ${CC} helloworld.c -o helloworld
}

do_install() {
        install -d ${D}${bindir}
        install -m 0755 helloworld ${D}${bindir}
}
```

The `do_compile` and `do_install` code blocks provide the Shell Scripting commands to build and install the resulting binary into the destination directory that is referenced as `${D}`.

However, in the case of an Autotools-based project, we can avoid a lot of code duplication using the `autotools` class in the stripped example extracted from the recipe `poky/meta/recipes-core/dbus-wait/dbus-wait_git.bb`, as follows:

```
DESCRIPTION = "A simple tool to wait for a specific signal over DBus"
...
inherit autotools
```

The simple act of inheriting the class is in fact providing all the code required to do the following tasks:

- Updating the configure script code and artifacts
- Updating the `libtool` scripts
- Running the `configure` script
- Running `make`
- Running `make install`

The same concepts apply to other building tools, as is the case for CMake and QMake. The number of supported classes is growing, and it is expected that new ones will be included in every release to support new build systems and avoid code duplication.

Writing a machine definition

Creating a new machine to be used by Poky is a straightforward task. It essentially provides the information needed for a machine to work. The bootloader, kernel, and hardware support drivers must be checked before starting to integrate the board into the BSP layer.

The Yocto Project supports x86-32, x86-64, ARM32, ARM64, MIPS, MIPS64, and PowerPC, representing the most currently used embedded architectures.

The prevailing set of variables used in a machine definition is as follows:

- `TARGET_ARCH`: This sets the machine architecture, for example, ARM and i586
- `PREFERRED_PROVIDER_virtual/kernel`: This overrides the default kernel (`linux-yocto`) in case you need to use a specific one
- `SERIAL_CONSOLES`: This defines serial consoles and their speeds
- `MACHINE_FEATURES`: This describes hardware features, so the needed software stack is included in the images by default

- KERNEL_IMAGETYPE: This is used to choose the kernel image type, for example, zImage and uImage

- IMAGE_FSTYPES: This sets the generated filesystem image types, for example, tar.gz, ext4, and ubifs

You can see examples of machine definition files inside the Poky source code in meta-yocto-bsp/conf/machine/.

When describing a new machine, we should pay special attention to specific features supported by it in MACHINE_FEATURES. This way, the needed software to support these features is installed into the images. The current available values for MACHINE_FEATURES are listed as follows:

- acpi: This indicates that the hardware has ACPI (x86/x86_64 only)

- alsa: This indicates that the hardware has ALSA audio drivers

- apm: This indicates that the hardware uses APM (or APM emulation)

- bluetooth: This indicates that the hardware has integrated Bluetooth

- ext2: This indicates that the hardware has HDD or microdrive

- irda: This indicates that the hardware has an IrDA support

- keyboard: This indicates that the hardware has a keyboard

- pci: This indicates that the hardware has a PCI bus

- pcmcia: This indicates that the hardware has PCMCIA or CompactFlash sockets

- screen: This indicates that the hardware has a screen

- serial: This indicates that the hardware has serial support (usually RS232)

- touchscreen: This indicates that the hardware has a touchscreen

- usbgadget: This indicates that the hardware is compatible with USB gadget devices

- usbhost: This indicates that the hardware is compatible with the USB host

- wifi: This indicates that the hardware has integrated Wi-Fi

Using a custom distribution

The creation of a distribution is a mix of simplicity and complexity. The process of creating the distribution file is very easy; however, the distribution configuration has a high impact in the way Poky behaves and may cause a binary incompatibility with previously built binaries, depending on the options we use.

The distribution is where we define global options such as the toolchain version, graphical backends, support for OpenGL, and so on. We should make a distribution only in case the default settings provided by Poky do not fulfill our requirements.

Usually, we intend to change a small set of options from Poky. For example, we remove the X11 support to use **framebuffer** instead. We can easily accomplish this reusing Poky distribution and overriding the variables we need. For example, the sample distribution represented by the file `<layer>/conf/distro/mydistro.conf` is as follows:

```
require conf/distro/poky.conf

DISTRO = "mydistro"
DISTRO_NAME = "mydistro (My New Distro)"
DISTRO_VERSION = "1.0"
DISTRO_CODENAME = "codename"
SDK_VENDOR = "-mydistrosdk"
SDK_VERSION := "${@'${DISTRO_VERSION}'.replace('snapshot-
${DATE}','snapshot')}"

MAINTAINER = "mydistro <mydistro@mycompany.com>"

DISTRO_FEATURES_remove = "x11"
```

To use the distribution just created, we need to add the following piece of code in `build/conf/local.conf`:

```
DISTRO = "mydistro"
```

The variable `DISTRO_FEATURES` may influence how the recipes are configured and the packages are installed in images. For example, if we want to be able to use sound in any machine and image, the `alsa` features must be present. The following list shows the present state for `DISTRO_FEATURES` supported values:

- `alsa`: This includes ALSA support (OSS compatibility kernel modules installed, if available).
- `bluetooth`: This includes Bluetooth support (integrated BT only).
- `cramfs`: This includes CramFS support.
- `ext2`: This includes tools to support devices with internal HDD/microdrives to store files (instead of flash-only devices).
- `ipsec`: This includes IPSec support.
- `ipv6`: This includes IPv6 support.
- `irda`: This includes IrDA support.

- `keyboard`: This includes keyboard support (for example, keymaps will be loaded during boot).

- `nfs`: This includes NFS client support (to mount NFS exports on devices).

- `opengl`: This includes the Open Graphics Library, a cross-language, multiplatform application programming interface used for rendering two- and three-dimensional graphics.

- `pci`: This includes PCI bus support.

- `pcmcia`: This includes the `PCMCIA`/`CompactFlash` support.

- `ppp`: This includes PPP dialup support.

- `smbfs`: This includes SMB networks client support (to mount Samba/ Microsoft Windows shares on devices).

- `systemd`: This includes support for the init manager, a full replacement of init with parallel starting of services, reduced shell overhead, and other features. This init manager is used by many distributions.

- `usbgadget`: This includes USB gadget device support (for USB networking/ serial/storage).

- `usbhost`: This includes USB host support (allows the connection of an external keyboard, mouse, storage, network, and so on).

- `wayland`: This includes the Wayland display server protocol and the library that supports it.

- `wifi`: This includes Wi-Fi support (integrated only).

Machine features versus distro features

Both `DISTRO_FEATURES` and `MACHINE_FEATURES` work together to provide feasible support on the final system.

When a machine supports a feature, this does not imply it is being supported by the final system because the distribution used must provide the underlying base for it.

If a machine supports Wi-Fi but the distribution does not, the applications used by the operating system will be built with Wi-Fi support disabled so that the outcome will be a system without Wi-Fi support.

On the other hand, if the distribution provides Wi-Fi support and a machine does not, the modules and applications needed for the Wi-Fi will not be installed in images built for this machine, though the operating system and its modules have support for Wi-Fi enabled.

Understanding the variables scope

The BitBake metadata has thousands of variables, but the scope where these variables are available depends on where it is defined. Basically, there are two kinds of variables as follows:

- Variables defined in configuration files are global to every recipe. The parsing order of the main configuration files is shown as follows:

    - ° `build/conf/local.conf`

    - ° `<layer>/conf/machines/<machine>.conf`

    - ° `<layer>/conf/distro/<distro>.conf`

- Variables defined within recipe files are local to the specific recipe only during the execution of its tasks.

Summary

In this chapter, we learned the reasons that motivate us to create a new layer and metadata. We saw a description on how to create machine configuration, a distribution definition, and recipes files. We learned how we can create images and how to include our application to an image.

In the next chapter, we will access some examples of the most common customization cases used by an additional layer, such as modifying existing packages, adding extra options to `autoconf`, applying a new patch, and including a new file to a package. We will see how to configure **BusyBox** and `linux-yocto`, two packages commonly customized when making an embedded system.

12
Customizing Existing Recipes

In the course of our work with Yocto Project's tools, it is expected that we need to customize existing recipes. In this chapter, we explore some examples, such as changing compilation options, enabling or disabling features of a recipe, applying an extra patch, and modifying **BusyBox** and **Linux Yocto Framework** settings.

Common use cases

Nowadays, projects usually have a set of layers to provide the required features; we certainly need to make changes on top of them, to adapt them to our specific needs. It may be cosmetic or substantive changes, but the way to accomplish them is the same.

To make changes to a preexisting recipe, we need to create a `.bbappend` file in our project layer. The name of the file is the same as the original recipe along with the *append* suffix. For example, if the original recipe was named `<original-layer>/recipes-core/app/app_1.0.bb`, our respective `.bbappend` will be `<layer>/recipes-core/app/app_1.0.bbappend`.

The `.bbappend` file can be seen as a piece of text that is appended at the end of the original recipe. It empowers us with an extremely flexible mechanism to avoid duplicating source code in order to apply the needed changes in our project's layers.

 When there is more than one `.bbappend` file for a recipe, all of them are joined following the layer priority order.

Adding extra options to recipes based on Autoconf

Let's assume we have Autoconf's build system-based application with a preexisting recipe for it, and we want to do the following:

- Enable `my-feature`
- Disable `another-feature`

The content of the `.bbappend` file, in order to make the changes, will be the following:

```
EXTRA_OECONF += "--enable-my-feature --disable-another-feature"
EXTRA_OEMAKE += "DEFINE_PASSED_TO_MAKE=1"
```

The same can also be done based on the hardware we are building for, as follows:

```
EXTRA_OECONF_append_arm = " --enable-my-arm-feature"
EXTRA_OEMAKE_append_mymachine = " MYMACHINE_SPECIFIC=1"
```

> `EXTRA_OECONF` is used to add extra options to the `configure` script.
>
> `EXTRA_OEMAKE` is used to add extra parameters to the `make` call.

Applying a patch

For cases when we need to apply some patch over an existent package, we should use `FILESEXTRAPATHS`, which includes new directories into the searching algorithm, making the extra file visible to BitBake, as shown:

```
FILESEXTRAPATHS_prepend := "${THISDIR}/${PN}-${PV}:"
SRC_URI += "file://mypatch.patch"
```

In the preceding example, the current directory / package version (`${THISDIR}/${PN}-${PV}:`) is included in the directories list used for file searching. The use of the `_prepend` operator is important as it guarantees that our provided file is used, even if a file with the same name is added in the lower priority layers in future.

BitBake assumes that every file with a `.patch` extension is a patch and applies it accordingly.

Adding extra files to the existing packages

If we need to include an extra configuration file, we should use FILESEXTRAPATHS, as explained in the previous example and shown in the following lines of code:

```
FILESEXTRAPATHS_prepend := "${THISDIR}/${PN}-${PV}:"

SRC_URI += "file://newconfigfile.conf"

do_install_append() {
    install -m 644 ${WORKDIR}/newconfig.conf ${D}${sysconfdir}
}
```

The do_install_append function appends the provided block below the metadata already available in the original do_install function. It includes the command needed to copy our new configuration file into the package filesystem. The file is copied from ${WORKDIR} to ${D} as the directory used by Poky to build the package and the destination directory used by Poky to create the package. The ${sysconfdir} directory is the system configuration directory (usually with /etc).

We should use the variables provided on top of poky/meta/conf/bitbake.conf instead of pointing to hardcoded paths. For example, use ${sysconfdir} instead of /etc and ${bindir} in place of /usr/bin.

Understanding file searching paths

When a file (a patch or a generic file) is included in SRC_URI, BitBake searches it in the variables FILESPATH and FILESEXTRAPTH. The default setting is to look in the following:

- `<recipe>-<version>/`
- `<recipe>/`
- `files/`

Besides this, it also checks for OVERRIDES for an override's specific file in each place. To illustrate this, consider a recipe foo_1.0.bb and the variable OVERRIDES = "<board>:<arch>"; the file will be searched in the following:

- `foo-1.0/<board>/`
- `foo-1.0/<arch>/`
- `foo-1.0/`

- `foo/<board>/`
- `foo/<arch>/`
- `foo/`
- `files/<board>/`
- `files/<arch>/`
- `files/`

This is just illustrative as the list of OVERRIDES is huge and machine-specific. When we work with our recipe, we can use `bitbake -e` in order to know the full list of available overrides for a specific machine and use it accordingly.

Changing recipe feature configuration

One supported mechanism to ease feature-set customization for recipes is PACKAGECONFIG. It provides a way to enable and disable the recipe features. For example, if the recipe has the following configuration:

```
PACKAGECONFIG ?= "feature1"
PACKAGECONFIG[feature1] = "--enable-feature1,--disable-
feature1,feature1depends"
PACKAGECONFIG[feature2] = "--enable-feature2,--disable-
feature2,feature2depends"
```

The recipe has two features, `feature1` and `feature2`. For each configuration option, there is a string to define how to enable the feature on `autoconf`, how to disable the feature on `autoconf`, and the new dependencies in case the option is enabled.

We can create a `.bbappend` file that expands the PACKAGECONFIG variable's default value to enable `feature2` as well, as shown:

```
PACKAGECONFIG += "feature2"
```

> In order to add the same feature in the `build/conf/local.conf` file, we can use PACKAGECONFIG_pn-<recipename>_append = 'feature2'.

More detailed information about the use of PACKAGECONFIG and its options can be found in the *Yocto Project Reference Manual*.

Customizing BusyBox

BusyBox is a key component of most embedded Linux-based projects as it provides an alternative with a smaller footprint when compared to the usual Linux counterparts for the most commonly used utilities. It can be seen as a Swiss knife since it provides a huge set of utilities and is quite flexible regarding which utilities to enable or disable. Poky provides a default setting for BusyBox, and it sometimes may not fulfill our needs; so, changing this configuration is a common task. For example, the `<layer>/recipes-core/busybox/busybox_1.22.1.bbappend` file could have the following lines of code:

```
FILESEXTRAPATHS_prepend := "${THISDIR}/${PN}:"
SRC_URI += "file://enable-tftpd.cfg"
```

The `<layer>/recipes-core/busybox/busybox/enable-tftpd.cfg` file contains the following:

```
CONFIG_TFTPD=y
```

This combination of the `.bbappend` file and configuration file is enough to enable support for the **TFTP** server in BusyBox.

 For the cases when we want to deselect an option, we can add a negative line instead, for example, `CONFIG_TFTPD=n`.

Customizing the linux-yocto framework

The Linux kernel is a complex software that provides an infinite number of possible configurations. The Yocto Project provides a framework (`linux-yocto`) to manage a huge set of machines in a single kernel tree. We can take advantage of this framework to enable or disable features for our machine, for example, by using `<layer>/recipes-kernel/linux/linux-yocto_3.14.bbappend` with the following content:

```
FILESEXTRAPATHS_prepend := "${THISDIR}/${PN}:"
SRC_URI += "file://enable-can.cfg"
```

The content of the `<layer>/recipes-kernel/linux/linux-yocto/linux-yocto/enable-can.cfg` file is as shown:

```
CONFIG_CAN=y
```

One common requirement when doing a Linux-based embedded system is to change the kernel configuration. We can do this using the SDK or BitBake, as explained:

- **Using SDK**: The creation and installation of the Yocto Project's SDK is detailed in *Chapter 8, Developing with the Yocto Project*. After having the SDK exported, we can configure the Linux kernel source in the usual way (for example, make menuconfig).

- **Using BitBake**: When small changes or testing is needed, we can use BitBake to configure or generate the Linux kernel configuration file. We can use the following command lines to achieve this:

```
$: bitbake virtual/kernel -c menuconfig
$: bitbake virtual/kernel -c savedefconfig
```

For Linux kernel development, the use of SDK is preferred as it provides a convenient development environment; BitBake should be used only for quick changes.

 We need to bear in mind that not every supported machine in the Yocto Project, vendor, and community BSP layers use the linux-yocto framework. This means that the configuration fragment mechanism is not available for those machines, and we need to provide a full defconfig file in order to customize their kernel.

The complete linux-yocto documentation can be found in the *Yocto Project Linux Kernel Development Manual*, which covers all aspects of the linux-yocto framework and advanced Linux kernel maintenance concepts.

Summary

In this chapter, we learned how we can customize existing recipes using the .bbappend files and benefit from this to avoid duplicating source code. We saw how to enable or disable one feature, how to apply a patch, and how to change BusyBox and the linux-yocto framework configuration.

In the next chapter, we will discuss how the Yocto Project can help us with some legal aspects of producing a Linux-based system using packages under different licenses. We will understand which artifacts we need and how Poky can be configured to generate the needed artifacts that should be shared as part of the copyleft compliance accomplishment process.

Achieving GPL Compliance

13

In this chapter, we learn how to fulfill open source license compliance and how we can use Poky to provide the needed artifacts such as source code, licensing text, and the list of derivative work. This is critical for most products being introduced in the market nowadays as open source code needs to live side-by-side with proprietary code.

Understanding copyleft

Copyleft is a legal way to use the copyright law in order to maximize rights and express freedom. It impacts our day-to-day work in such a way that companies must know how to deal with open source and free software licenses as they have a high impact on their products.

When building a Linux distribution, there are at least two projects being used: the Linux kernel and a compiler. The most commonly used compiler nowadays is the **GNU Compiler Collection (GCC)**.

The Linux kernel is released under the **GPLv2** license, and the GCC is released under the **GPLv2**, **GPLv2.1**, and **GPLv3** licenses, depending on the project used.

However, a Linux-based system can virtually include all projects available throughout the world, in addition to all applications made by the company for its product. How do we know the number of projects and licenses, and how do we fulfill copyleft compliance requirements?

 This chapter describes how the Yocto Project can help you in the task, but be aware that you must know exactly what you need to provide and the possible license incompatibilities. If you have any doubts, please consult your legal department or a copyright lawyer.

In this chapter, we understand how the Yocto Project can help us with the most common tasks required for copyleft compliance.

Copyleft compliance versus proprietary code

It is important to understand that proprietary code and copyleft-covered code can coexist in the same product. We need to be careful about the libraries we link the code with because some may have license compatibility issues. However, this is the standard in most of the available products in the market nowadays.

Some guidelines for license compliance

As already mentioned, one Linux-based system is a set of several projects, each one under a different license. The Yocto Project helps developers understand that most copyleft project obligations have the following conditions:

- The source code of the project must be provided along with the binary
- The license of the project must be provided along with the binary
- Any modification in the project or any script needed to configure and build it must be provided along with the binary

It means that if, one project under copyleft is modified, the license text, the base source code, and any modification must be included into the final deliverable.

The assumptions cover most rights guaranteed by copyleft licenses. These are the parts where the Yocto Project may help us. However, before releasing anything, we are recommended to audit all the materials to be released to make sure they're complete.

Managing software licensing with Poky

One important Poky feature is the capability of license for license management. Most of the time, we, as developers, do not care about licenses because we keep our focus on our own bugs. However, when creating a product, it is very important to care and know about licenses and the kind of licenses present in it.

Poky keeps track of licenses, works with commercial and noncommercial licenses, and has a strategy to work with proprietary applications, at least during the development cycle.

One important thing to know, at first, is that a recipe is released under a certain license, and it represents a project released under a different license. The recipe and the project are two different entities and they have different licensing, so the two different licenses must be considered part of the product.

In most recipes, information is a comment with the copyright, license, and author name; this information is regarding the recipe itself. Then, there is a set of variables to describe the package license, and they are as follows:

- LICENSE: This describes the license under which the package was released.
- LIC_FILES_CHKSUM: This may not seem very useful at first sight. It describes the license file and its checksum for a package, and we may find a lot of variation on how a project describes its license. The most common license files are stored in `meta/files/common-licenses/`.

Some projects include a file, such as COPYING or LICENSE; others use a header note on each file or on the main file. The variable LIC_FILES_CHKSUM has the checksum for the license text of a project; if any letters are changed, the checksum is changed as well. This is used to make sure any change is noted and consciously accepted by the developer. A license change may be a typo fix; however, it may also be a change in legal obligations. So, it is important for the developer to review and understand the change.

When a different license checksum is detected, BitBake launches a build error and points to the project that had its license changed. You must be careful when this happens as the license change may impact the use of this software. In order to be able to build anything again, you must change the LIC_FILE_CHKSUM value accordingly and update the LICENSE field to match the license change. Your legal department should be consulted if the license terms have changed.

Commercial licenses

By default, Poky does not install any package with a commercial license restriction. The most used example is the `gst-plugins-ugly` package. This limitation is archived though a variable used on these recipes with some license restriction; the LICENSE_FLAGS variable is used to determinate the restriction.

In the `gst-plugins-ugly` case, the variable in the recipe is set to LICENSE_FLAGS = "commercial", although it may have a string. Some projects choose to set it to LICENSE_FLAGS = "<license>_${PN}_${PV}".

In order to install these recipes, we must place a whitelist of desired special licensing on `build/conf/local.conf`, and we can do this using `LICENSE_FLAGS_WHITELIST`. This variable determines the special license that can be used and has a very flexible content.

For example, for **GStreamer Ugly Plug-ins**, we may only want this package to be installed, so we add the following variable in `build/conf/local.conf`, as shown:

```
LICENSE_FLAGS_WHITELIST = "commercial_gst-plugins-ugly"
```

This exclude any other commercial recipe such as `gst-plugins-bad`. However, if we want BitBake to install any commercial package from our image, we may use the following code in `build/conf/local.conf`:

```
LICENSE_FLAGS_WHITELIST = "commercial"
```

Using Poky to achieve copyleft compliance

At this point, we know how to use Poky and understand its main goal. It is time to understand the legal aspects of producing a Linux-based system that uses packages under different licenses.

We can configure Poky to generate the needed artifacts that should be shared as part of the copyleft compliance accomplishment process.

License auditing

To help us to achieve copyleft compliance, Poky generates a license manifest during the image build located at `build/tmp/deploy/licenses/<image_name-machine_name-datestamp>/`.

To demonstrate this process, we use the `core-image-full-cmdline` image for the `qemuarm` machine. To start with our example, examine the files under `build/tmp/deploy/licenses/core-image-full-cmdline-qemuarm-<datastamp>`, which are as follows:

- `package.manifest`: This lists all the packages into the image.
- `license.manifest`: This lists the names, versions, recipe names, and licenses for all packages. This file may be used for copyleft compliance auditing.

Providing the source code

The first obvious way Poky may help us to provide the source code of every project used on our image is by sharing the `DL_DIR` content. However, this approach has one important pitfall. Any proprietary source code will be shared within `DL_DIR` if it is shared as is. In addition, this approach will share any source code, including the ones that are not required by copyleft compliance.

Another way is to configure Poky to generate the set of source code and decide what will be delivered. It may be done using the `Archiver` class. This class copies the source code for each package under the `build/tmp/deploy` folder separated by architecture (in our example, the present architectures are `allarch-poky-linux`, `arm-poky-linux-gnueabi`, and `x86_64-linux`) and license. The package for `arm-poky-linux-gnueabi` released under GPLv3 is placed in the `build/tmp/deploy/sources/arm-poky-linux-gnueabi/GPLv3/package-name` directory.

Poky must be configured to archive the source code before the final image is created. So, in order to have it, we can paste the following variables in `build/conf/local.conf`:

```
INHERIT += "archiver"
ARCHIVER_MODE[src] = "original"
```

Keep in mind that, even with this approach, if we share the `build/tmp/deploy/sources` directories, the proprietary unneeded sources are shared, although we may now choose to share the source based on licensing. We can copy only the packages under GPLv3 or MIT to a shareable place, or to any other combination of licensing, according to the desired sharing strategy.

One example of a copy command line, used to copy all packages under any GPL license (from the *Yocto Project Development Manual*) is the following:

```
$: cd poky/build/tmp/deploy/sources
$: mkdir ~/gpl_source_release
$: for dir in */*GPL*; do cp -r $dir ~/gpl_source_release; done
```

If we prefer to take some help from Poky regarding which license must have our attention, we can add the `ARCHIVER_MODE[filter] ?= "yes"` code to `build/conf/local.conf`. The default configuration is to have source code for every project, in other words, no filter. However, if we prefer to have only the source code for `COPYLEFT_LICENSE_INCLUDE` projects, we can use a filter.

The COPYLEFT_LICENSE_INCLUDE variable currently includes all licenses starting with GPL or LGPL. This variable can be overridden in build/conf/local.conf, if we wish to make sure to include another license or variation.

Providing compilation scripts and source code modifications

With the configuration provided in the previous section, Poky will package the original source code for each project. In case we want to include the patched source code, we only use ARCHIVER_MODE[src] = "patched"; this way, Poky will wrap the project source code after the do_patch task. It includes modifications from recipes or the bbappend file.

This way, the source code and any modification may be shared easily. However, there is still one kind of information not created so far: the procedure used to configure and build the project.

In order to have a reproducible build environment, we may share the configured project; in other words, the project after the do_configure task. For this, we can add the following to build/conf/local.conf:

```
ARCHIVER_MODE[src] = "configured"
```

It is important to remember that we must consider the person on the other side may not use the Yocto Project for copyleft compliance; alternatively, if they are using it, they must know that the modification made on the original source code and configuration procedure is not available. This is the reason to share the configured project. It allows anyone to reproduce our build environment.

For all flavors of source code, the default resultant file is a tarball; other options will add ARCHIVER_MODE[srpm] = "1" in build/conf/local.conf, and the resultant file will be a SRPM package.

Providing license text

When providing the source code, the license text is shared inside it. If we want the license text inside our final image, we can add the following to build/conf/local.conf:

```
COPY_LIC_MANIFEST = "1"
COPY_LIC_DIRS = "1"
```

This way, the license files will be placed inside the root filesystem, under /usr/share/common-licenses/.

Summary

In this chapter, we learned how Poky can help with copyleft license compliance accomplishment and also understood why it *should not* be used as a legal background. Poky enables us to generate source code, reproduction scripts, and license text for used packages, to be used in our distribution. In addition, we learned that the license manifest generated within the image may be used to audit the image.

In the next chapter, we will understand how we can use the Yocto Project tools with an external BSP, the **Freescale** ARM BSP. We will use it to generate an image for use with the **Wandboard** machine.

14
Booting Our Custom Embedded Linux

It's time! We are now ready to boot our custom-made embedded Linux as we have learned the required concepts and gained enough knowledge about the Yocto Project and Poky. In this chapter, we practice what we have learned so far about using Poky with an external BSP, the Freescale ARM BSP, use it to generate an image for use with the Wandboard machine, and boot it using the SD card.

The same concepts can be applied to every other board, as long as a vendor provides a BSP layer to use with the Yocto Project.

We can see a list of the most commonly used BSP layers in this chapter. This should not be taken as a complete list, or as a definitive one, but we want to facilitate your search for the needed layer in case you have one board of a specific vendor next to you. This list is as follows, in alphabetic order:

- **Allwinner**: This has the `meta-allwinner` layer
- **BeagleBoard**: This has the `meta-beagleboard` layer
- **CuBox-i**: This has the `meta-fsl-arm-extra` layer
- **Intel**: This has the `meta-intel` layer
- **Raspberry Pi**: This has the `meta-raspberrypi` layer
- **Texas Instruments**: This has the `meta-ti` layer
- **Wandboard**: This has the `meta-fsl-arm-extra` layer

Exploring the Wandboard

The **Wandboard** is a not-for-profit low-cost **Cortex-A9** processor, based on the Freescale i.MX6 SoC board with high-performance multimedia capabilities. The board is available in three versions, as shown in the following table:

Board version	Features
Wandboard Solo	Freescale i.MX6S processor (single-core)
	512 MB RAM
Wandboard Dual	Freescale i.MX6DL processor (dual-core)
	1 GB RAM
	802.11n wireless and Bluetooth
Wandboard Quad	Freescale i.MX6Q processor (quad-core)
	2 GB RAM
	802.11n wireless and Bluetooth
	SATA

The Wandboard is supported by the Wandboard community. More information is available at `http://www.wandboard.org/`. The following is an image of a Wandboard:

Discovering Freescale ARM BSP

The Wandboard board uses the Freescale i.MX6 SoC. To use it with the Yocto Project, we need to use BSP layers.

The needed BSP layers to enable Wandboard support in Yocto Project are the following:

- `meta-fsl-arm`: This BSP layer adds support to Freescale's reference machines and provides the basic BSP support

- `meta-fsl-arm-extra`: This BSP layer adds support to third-party boards based on Freescale's SoC, such as Wandboard, and requires `meta-fsl-arm` as it provides the base BSP support

Freescale BSP is supported by a community, and more information on it can be found at `http://freescale.github.io/`.

Using Wandboard with the Yocto Project

The modular structure of the Yocto Project gives us the freedom to include external BSP layers to extend a set of supported machines.

The first step to enable support for Wandboard is to download the metadata of the BSP layers.

From the directory where the Poky source code is cloned, please run the following command lines:

```
$: git clone --branch daisy https://github.com/Freescale/meta-fsl-arm-
extra.git
$: git clone --branch daisy git://git.yoctoproject.org/meta-fsl-arm
```

The final directory structure you should have is shown in the following figure:

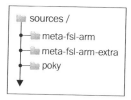

After completing this, we must create the build directory we use for our builds. We can do this using the following command line:

```
$: source poky/oe-init-build-env build-wandboard
```

 The same procedure was first introduced in *Chapter 2, Baking Our Poky-based System.*

Some packages included in Freescale ARM BSP have proprietary property and are followed by a **End-user License Agreement (EULA)** that shows the legal impact of using it. Mainly, the GPU drivers, VPU/IPU codecs, and the `meta-fsl-arm` layer have an EULA file that describes the rights and obligations to use the binaries and source. Read more on the EULA and in case you accept it, edit the `build/conf/local.conf` file in order to set `ACCEPT_FSL_EULA` to `1`, as shown in the following line of code:

```
ACCEPT_FSL_EULA = "1"
```

This is not required for the board to work, but for full use, the hardware features are indispensable.

Independently, whether or not we accept the EULA, we must edit the `build-wandboard/conf/bblayers.conf` file to enable the just cloned layers. The final file must look as follows:

```
conf/bblayers.conf for wandboard
# LAYER_CONF_VERSION is increased each time build/conf/bblayers.conf
# changes incompatibly
LCONF_VERSION = "6"

BBPATH = "${TOPDIR}"
BBFILES ?= ""

#BBLAYERS ?= " \
#   /home/user/yp/sources/poky/meta \
#   /home/user/yp/sources/poky/meta-yocto \
#   /home/user/yp/sources/poky/meta-yocto-bsp \
#   "
BBLAYERS_NON_REMOVABLE ?= " \
  /home/user/yp/sources/poky/meta \
  /home/user/yp/sources/poky/meta-yocto \
  "

BBLAYERS += " \
  /home/user/yp/sources/meta-fsl-arm \
  /home/user/yp/sources/meta-fsl-arm-extra \
  "
$: _
```

The procedure for adding an external layer was first introduced in *Chapter 10, Exploring External Layers*.

Building an image for Wandboard

After we have the build directory and the BSP layers are properly set up, we can start the build. Inside the `build-wandboard` directory, we must call the following command:

```
$: MACHINE=wandboard-<variant> bitbake <image>
```

The `MACHINE` variable can be changed depending on the Wandboard we want to use or set in `build/conf/local.conf`. The machine names for the Wandboard variants are `wandboard-solo`, `wandboard-dual`, and `wandboard-quad`.

If we want to use the Wandboard Solo and build `core-image-sato`, which provides an embedded graphical environment, we should run the following command:

```
$: MACHINE=wandboard-solo bitbake core-image-sato
```

The build process will take a while. It takes about 2 hours and about 10 Gigabytes in a workstation machine.

If you didn't accept the EULA or want a smaller image to build faster, you can build `core-image-minimal` instead. For this, use the following command:

```
$: MACHINE=wandboard-solo bitbake core-image-minimal
```

 In *Chapter 2, Baking Our Poky-based System*, there is a list of some possible images to be used.

Booting Wandboard from the SD card

After the build process is over, the image will be available inside the `build-wandboard/tmp/deploy/images/wandboard-solo/` directory. There are many files, but Freescale ARM BSP generates a ready-to-use SD card image.

The file we want to use is `core-image-sato-wandboard-solo.sdcard` or `core-image-minimal.sdcard`, depending on the image we built.

Make sure your point to the right device and double check to not write in your hard disk.

In order to copy the generated image to the SD card, we should use the dd utility, as follows:

```
$: sudo dd if=core-image-sato-wandboard-solo.sdcard of=/dev/sdX bs=1M
```

We can also use the following command:

```
$: sudo dd if=core-image-minimal-wandboard-solo.sdcard of=/dev/sdX bs=1M
```

After copying the content in the SD card, insert it into the SD card slot, connect the HDMI cable, and power on the machine. It should boot nicely.

 There are two SD card slots in Wandboard. The primary slot is located in the CPU board, used for booting, and a secondary slot is found in the peripheral board (the base board).

Summary

In this final chapter, we introduced two community projects, Wandboard and Freescale ARM BSP layers. We consolidated our Yocto Project knowledge by adding external BSP layers and using these in a real board with a generated image.

Throughout the book, we learned the needed background information for you to learn on your own any other aspect of the Yocto Project that you may need. You have the general understanding to know what is happening behind the scenes when you ask BitBake to build a recipe or an image. From now on, you are ready to free your mind and try new things. There are plenty of boards available, waiting for you to give them life. The ball is in your court now; here's where the fun begins!

References

The following are the references used in the book:

- Yocto Project Reference Manual: `http://www.yoctoproject.org/docs/1.6/ref-manual/ref-manual.html`

- BitBake Development mailing list: `bitbake-devel@lists.openembedded.org`

- OpenEmbedded-Core mailing list: `openembedded-core@lists.openembedded.org`

- Yocto Project Development Manual: `http://www.yoctoproject.org/docs/1.6/dev-manual/dev-manual.html`

- Yocto Project Git: `http://git.yoctoproject.org/`

- OpenEmbedded Layer Index: `http://layers.openembedded.org`

- BitBake User Manual: `http://www.yoctoproject.org/docs/1.6/bitbake-user-manual/bitbake-user-manual.html`

- Yocto Project Linux Kernel Development Manual: `http://www.yoctoproject.org/docs/1.6/kernel-dev/kernel-dev.html`

Index

postrm script 51
preinst script 51
prelink process 38
PREMIRRORS variable 33, 34
prepending, metadata 62
prerm script 51
PR variable 54
psplash 90
Python functions, metadata
  defining 64, 65
Python variable expansion, metadata 64

Q

QEMU
  about 19
  target image, executing in 19, 20
qemuarm directory 46
qemuarm-tcbootstrap directory 46
QMake 91
qt4e-demo-image 18
Quick EMUlator. *See* QEMU

R

RDEPENDS variable 29
recipe feature configuration
  modifying 100
recipes
  about 28
  preferring 30, 31
  providing 30, 31
Red Hat Package Manager 49
remote file downloads 31, 32
require directive 63
root filesystem image
  generating 37-39
rootfs image. *See* root filesystem image
RPM 38, 49
runqemu script 19
runtime dependency 29

S

SDK
  about 67, 68
  tracking, buildhistory used 74, 75

used, for modifying kernel
  configuration 102
shared state cache 49, 53
smart install command 57
smart query command 57
software development kit. *See* SDK
software layer 82
software licensing
  managing, Poky used 104, 105
source code
  fetching 31
  Git repository 32, 33
  network access, disabling 35
  other repositories 33
  remote file downloads 31, 32
source code download
  optimizing 33, 34
source code, layers
  detailing 83, 84
SRCREV variable 33
sstate-cache directory 41
sstate-cache package 53
supported package formats
  code, running 51
  DEB 50
  IPK 50
  RPM 49
  scripts, using 51, 52
  selecting 50
  TAR 50
  using 49
sysroots directory
  about 43, 46
  qemuarm directory 46
  qemuarm-tcbootstrap directory 46
  x86_64-linux directory 46

T

target image
  build-appliance-image 17
  building 17-19
  core-image-base 17
  core-image-clutter 18
  core-image-directfb 18
  core-image-full-cmdline 18
  core-image-lsb 18

Thank you for buying
Embedded Linux Development with Yocto Project

About Packt Publishing

Packt, pronounced 'packed', published its first book "*Mastering phpMyAdmin for Effective MySQL Management*" in April 2004 and subsequently continued to specialize in publishing highly focused books on specific technologies and solutions.

Our books and publications share the experiences of your fellow IT professionals in adapting and customizing today's systems, applications, and frameworks. Our solution based books give you the knowledge and power to customize the software and technologies you're using to get the job done. Packt books are more specific and less general than the IT books you have seen in the past. Our unique business model allows us to bring you more focused information, giving you more of what you need to know, and less of what you don't.

Packt is a modern, yet unique publishing company, which focuses on producing quality, cutting-edge books for communities of developers, administrators, and newbies alike. For more information, please visit our website: www.packtpub.com.

About Packt Open Source

In 2010, Packt launched two new brands, Packt Open Source and Packt Enterprise, in order to continue its focus on specialization. This book is part of the Packt Open Source brand, home to books published on software built around Open Source licenses, and offering information to anybody from advanced developers to budding web designers. The Open Source brand also runs Packt's Open Source Royalty Scheme, by which Packt gives a royalty to each Open Source project about whose software a book is sold.

Writing for Packt

We welcome all inquiries from people who are interested in authoring. Book proposals should be sent to author@packtpub.com. If your book idea is still at an early stage and you would like to discuss it first before writing a formal book proposal, contact us; one of our commissioning editors will get in touch with you.

We're not just looking for published authors; if you have strong technical skills but no writing experience, our experienced editors can help you develop a writing career, or simply get some additional reward for your expertise.

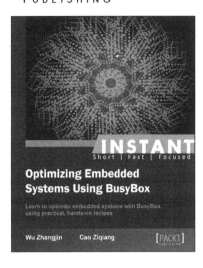

Instant Optimizing Embedded Systems Using BusyBox

ISBN: 978-1-78328-985-1   Paperback: 72 pages

Learn to optimize embedded systems with BusyBox using practical, hands-on recipes

1. Build and play embedded (Android Linux) system with BusyBox from scratch. Configure, compile, cross-compile, and install BusyBox.

2. Build external utilities and development environments (include Bash and C) for a BusyBox-based embedded system to meet diverse system requirements.

Linux Utilities Cookbook

ISBN: 978-1-78216-300-8   Paperback: 224 pages

Over 70 recipes to help you accomplish a wide variety of tasks in Linux quickly and efficiently

1. Use the command line like a pro.

2. Pick a suitable desktop environment.

3. Learn to use files and directories efficiently.

Please check **www.PacktPub.com** for information on our titles

BeagleBone Home Automation

ISBN: 978-1-78328-573-0   Paperback: 178 pages

Live your sophisticated dream with home automation using BeagleBone

1. Practical approach to home automation using BeagleBone; starting from the very basics of GPIO control and progressing up to building a complete home automation solution.

2. Covers the operating principles of a range of useful environment sensors, including their programming and integration to the server application.

Kali Linux – Assuring Security by Penetration Testing

ISBN: 978-1-84951-948-9   Paperback: 454 pages

Master the art of penetration testing with Kali Linux

1. Learn penetration testing techniques with an in-depth coverage of Kali Linux distribution.

2. Explore the insights and importance of testing your corporate network systems before the hackers strike.

3. Understand the practical spectrum of security tools by their exemplary usage, configuration, and benefits.

Please check **www.PacktPub.com** for information on our titles

42296779R00080

Made in the USA
Lexington, KY
15 June 2015